INTO THE FUNHOUSE

AN UNPREDICTABLE STORY OF A

RELENTLESS LEUKEMIA

WALTER HARP

ISBN: 978-0-9982068-3-7

LS Publishing, Inc.
Mercer Island, WA
98040
United States

For Angela

PREFACE

I should have died by now—on more than one occasion. Yet I remain alive almost a decade after diagnosis with acute leukemia.

I face a cancer that returns over and over while leading a "normal" life as a husband, dad, and working professional.

What follows is true, although I've changed most names. It's a story of cancer, one of endurance, one that speaks honestly and starkly of death.

I grew up healthy and energetic in the most placid of places—Des Moines, Iowa. When I wasn't in school, you could find me pedaling across the city's quiet middle-class neighborhoods on my blue banana-seat bike, playing "kill the man with the football" in my friends' grassy backyards, swimming in one of the city's decidedly chlorine-laden public pools, fishing in the pond of a sprawling cemetery near my house, sledding the snow-covered hills of local golf courses, or shooting hoops at the downtown YMCA. In high school, I wrestled in gyms in rural towns across the state and eventually advanced to team captain. I also made the varsity football team, although honestly I wasn't big enough or fast enough to garner much field time.

Health was never an issue in my family. As I write this, my paternal grandfather, a veteran of WWII, at age ninety-seven is still alive and as sharp, witty, charming, and flirtatious as ever. My great-aunt, now nearly one hundred, recently sent me the most endearing handwritten birthday card from Oklahoma. Both of my parents are still alive as well. All my siblings, my cousins, aunts, and uncles. All my close friends.

One exception to the trend: my stepfather, with whom I lived from fourth grade on after my parents divorced, suffered a heart embolism when I was a junior in high school and died almost instantly on our living-room floor. He was fifty-six.

A group of friends and I were playing basketball when a neighbor pulled into the driveway to fetch me. "Walt, you need to come with me. Bob is in the hospital."

I remember taking hold of Bob's lifeless hand as he lay face up on a gurney in a soundless blue room just off the hospital's emergency entrance. The two of us were alone. Nylon stitches held together the deep slices doctors had carved to open his chest in an attempt to revive his heart.

Wow...he's still warm.

When I was eight, I watched a man in the church where my step-father ministered go from a loud, boisterous, jovial jokester who dominated coffee hours in the building's basement to a silent invalid, left motionless in a rocking chair by ALS. The next year, another man, one who attended the same church as my biological father in rural Indiana, deteriorated from an ebullient, strapping giant to a sad, stooping scarecrow due to some form of cancer rumored to have come from exposure to Agent Orange in Vietnam. I can picture him sitting sullen and still in the bow of my father's fishing boat, his expressionless eyes obscured by large, dark, empty pockets.

Aside from those instances, I inhabited a world largely absent of illness. Disease never crossed my mind, except perhaps when it was referred to on television or touched on in biology class.

That certainly has changed.

PART I:
STEP RIGHT UP

JUST A BACKACHE

I plopped into the passenger seat of my mother-in-law's Toyota and lowered the back until I lay prone, hoping to alleviate the ache I had been feeling for hours. It was 3 p.m. on Halloween, a month after the fall of Lehman Brothers at the height of the 2007-2008 financial meltdown, when the market for mortgage bonds collapsed and, ultimately, the global economy toppled like Goliath. I had stayed home from work that day because of back pain, a new experience. My back *never* hurt.

Must have strained it at the gym yesterday. Haven't been doing much strength training. Wasn't warmed up enough.

Alice and I drove in silence.

In the far eastern reaches of Bellevue, a sizable Seattle suburb distinguished by its tall glass buildings rising over Lake Washington, we made our way to the modest medical office of Dr. Geraldine Venazzi. Once there, I waited, as usual, all of a minute before the receptionist took me to see her.

"Walter! You're looking good!" Dr. Venazzi beamed. "What's going on?"

"It's my back. I think I pulled something."

"Well, let's have a look!"

Dr. Venazzi told me to remove my shirt and, once it was off, she ran her hands over my back.

"This is where it hurts," I said, pointing between my

shoulder blades.

"On a scale of one to ten, how bad is the pain?"

"Around a four." I ached, but I wasn't in agony.

"Well, I don't see anything wrong. But let's get you an MRI to be sure."

Dr. Venazzi had her receptionist call Bellevue Medical Imaging to schedule an MRI for that night. She also wrote me a prescription for pain medication, one I never filled. As I passed by a drugstore on the way home, I entertained fleetingly the idea of going in for the meds, but passed. It didn't seem necessary. Not then.

That evening, my wife, Angela, called her mother, and asked her to take our two kids, Luke and Sofia, then both still tiny at five and two, trick-or-treating so she could drive me to the MRI. Again, Alice kindly obliged.

By the time we arrived at the clinic that night, the pain had grown significantly worse. I sprawled across one of the several rows of seats in the waiting area, thinking that might ease the ache. Angela sat across from me, watching me take shallow breaths. It hurt to expand my rib cage.

A technician distracted me from the pain when he opened a door to the reception area and called my name. "Walter?"

"Yes?" I raised my hand, even though Angela and I were the only people in the reception room.

The technician led me through the back hallways while

Angela sat out front and flipped somewhat anxiously through a recent issue of *People*.

"I need you to take off all of your clothes and put them with your other belongings in one of these lockers," the tech instructed. "I'll be back in a few minutes."

The light wood lockers were no wider than two fists, yet I still managed to stuff my jeans and sweatshirt inside.

The technician startled me from behind, saying, "Oh... and I forgot to mention you'll need to put on one of these gowns, too." He handed me the garment.

I managed to work through the pain to tie the gown behind my back, frustratingly blind to what I was doing. I grabbed a robe, which I knew from experience to wear to keep from exposing my buttocks to anyone behind me, since hospital garments part like curtains in the rear. Not that I was particularly modest. Or ashamed. At five foot eight and nearly 190 pounds, I was mostly muscle, in spite of the aspiring love handles at my waist.

When the technician returned, he asked me to follow him down the hall, where we entered a low-lit room. A giant plastic igloo loomed in the corner.

Must be expensive. I wonder what one of those things costs. And how did they get it in here?

The technician gestured to the stretcher resting on rails that jutted out from the igloo's entrance. "Hop up and lie down," he instructed before packing me into the stretcher like a fish in ice, binding my feet and pressing my head into a vice made of foam.

"Would you like some music?"

Why not? It'll help pass the time.

"Sure," I said.

"Classical or modern rock?"

Modern rock? No. "Classical," I replied. In 2008, whether it was a modern-rock channel on an airplane or in a dentist's office—or in this case, an MRI clinic—you were lucky to recognize any of the songs, all of which were awful. Pandora was yet to exist, so you were stuck with whatever playlist some masochist had preprogrammed. The tech wrapped thin plastic headphones over my head and placed a hard rubber lemon tethered to a long cord into my hand.

"We're going to take seven sets of pictures. It'll take about forty-five minutes. I'll be right on the other side of the wall. You'll hear me, and I'll hear you, but you can squeeze this ball if there's an emergency."

The tech left the room and spoke to me over the headphones.

"You ready?" His voice, broken up by static, suddenly filled my head.

"Yes."

The stretcher underneath me jerked forward like a roller coaster coming out of the gate.

Lurch—pause...lurch—pause.

Traveling headfirst into the igloo, I could see its open maw inching closer and closer overhead until ultimately it swallowed me whole.

It's really, really tight in here. I didn't like the feeling. My heart rate went up, and once again the technician's muffled voice crackled through the headphones.

"Mr. Harp, we're ready to start. Each session will take three to five minutes. You're going to hear a lot of loud noise."

The downside of choosing the classical music channel was that it was a relentless chaotic traffic jam of loud drums, blaring horns, and high-pitched violins. Nothing subtle. Nothing melodic, like Vivaldi or Bach. Just violent, Tchaikovsky-esque cacophonies—like Disney's *Fantasia* gone wrong.

Boom! Boom! Crash!

Searing violins! Storming horns!

Crash! Boom!

The MRI came to life.

BZZZZZ! BANG!

Minutes passed as the noise pressed on, the loud pops and rattle of the MRI machine accompanied by a jolting and dramatic symphonic stew.

BANG! BUMP!

Sawing cellos! Shattering timpani!

The air began to feel warm and increasingly humid. *Something's wrong.* As the harsh sounds raged in my ears, the air thickened from a broth to a cream and I started to feel alarmed that my face was practically flush with the smooth, rounded ceiling of the tunnel that held me trapped, unable to move.

Why is it so freakin' hot in here?

Barely room to breathe.

This isn't right...something is definitely wrong.

I squeezed the rubber lemon, and within seconds the screeching car wreck in my ears came to a halt. The technician's voice reverberated with an electric crack.

"Yes, Mr. Harp?"

"I can't breathe in here," I said, a little panicked.

The technician said nothing for what seemed a good while.

"Can you hear me?"

"Is that better?" he finally replied.

I felt a light breeze brush over my face and into my nostrils.

"Much better," I said, relieved.

I can breathe...

It turned out the technician had forgotten to turn on the

fan inside what had become a terrarium.

"Ready to continue?"

"Yes, but can you tell me when each session is done?" I didn't want to spend the next forty-five minutes wondering anxiously when this would end.

"Of course. Are you ready?"

I couldn't take it anymore, so I sat up in the bed, wrapped my arms around my knees, and started to rock. Angela and I were back at home. Three hours had passed since the MRI, and what was once a mere ache had become excruciating. My ribs, hips, and scapula throbbed in rhythm with my heartbeat. I didn't know at the time that my bones were packed with leukemic blasts (cancerous white blood cells)—billions upon billions of them. And they were multiplying. As the population grew, the volume of blasts pressed against the inside of my bones like magma against the Earth's crust. I had never felt such torment in my life.

"Are you ok?" Angela asked, her eyes full of concern. "Do you want me to take you to the emergency room?"

"Yes. Let's go," I said with certainty, despite the fact I'd never been inside an ER. The agony was *overwhelming* now.

Angela called Alice again and she came to watch our little ones, who at midnight were fast asleep, dreaming of the troves of Halloween candy they had amassed from houses on our block. The moment Alice arrived, Angela and I jumped into the Subaru and beelined it to nearby Overlake Hospital, where minutes later we walked through the automatic sliding glass doors into the emergency room.

No one was waiting in the ER's reception area, which made the small admissions desk in the middle appear even smaller. We were admitted right away.

"Mr. Harp..." began the nurse.

"Please call me Walt," I gently interrupted.

"On a scale of one to ten, how would you rate your pain?"

"Ten," I replied without having to think.

"How long have you had it?"

"It's been building over the last day or so."

"OK. Let's get you something for that." The nurse left and returned with an IV prep kit.

"What are you giving me?" I asked as she pushed the needle into the crook of my right arm.

"Dilaudid. It'll help with the pain."

And sure enough, it did. Instant, blessed relief.

"What'd you give me?" I asked again, feeling a little hazy and forgetting I had just asked the same question.

"Dilaudid," the nurse told me a second time.

I fell asleep.

An hour later, I opened my eyes when I felt something

brush against the side of the bed and discovered the ER's attending physician standing over me.

"I hear you're having some pain," she said quietly.

"I was when I first got here—quite a bit."

"How are you feeling now?"

"Much better." I had already forgotten the malady. Everything felt fine, except for the fact I was in the ER.

"On a scale of one to ten, how would you describe your pain?"

"Zero."

"OK. That's good to hear. I'd still like to run a few tests, though."

Angela, who had been wilting from the late hour in a low, brown, imitation-leather chair, perked up at the mention of tests. "Is he ok?"

"He's fine. I just want to do some blood work."

Not a short while later, the clock on the wall said 4:05 a.m. I looked over at Angela, who was now asleep, and whispered, "Why don't you go home?" just loud enough to wake her. "This could take a while. I can take a taxi home."

"I should stay," she said sleepily.

"Nothing's going to happen here. They're just gonna run a few tests. Might as well get some rest. One of us is going to need to be up with the kids tomorrow."

"You sure?"

"Positive."

Angela stood to leave. "OK. I love you," she said, pecking me with fish lips and leaving the room, unaware we were about to embark on a ruthless endurance test.

When I next squinted at the clock, it read 5:30 a.m.

Why am I still here? I wasn't in pain anymore. Time to go home, yes?

The physician returned. "Mr. Harp, your platelet count is low," she told me unceremoniously. "It's fifty thousand."

Um....

I knew what platelets were, but I didn't know what to make of the number. "I'm not sure I understand."

"The platelet level in your blood is quite low. You should get it checked out."

OK.

This all seemed harmless enough. That is, until I later learned that the normal platelet volume is 150,000 to 450,000 platelets per microliter of blood[1]. At 50,000, my platelet count was *very* low—and, unbeknownst to any of us, getting lower by the minute.

"Who is your primary care physician?"

---

1   Remember platelets from high school biology? They keep blood thick and, when exposed to oxygen, congeal and harden to stop bleeding. Without enough platelets, blood won't clot. Without any platelets at all, blood will seep through the capillaries and you will die from internal hemorrhaging.

"Geraldine Venazzi. She's here in Bellevue."

"I would make an appointment to see her."

Ugh. Another doctor's appointment.

HOBBLED

While the whole ER thing was new to me that night, I wasn't a virgin when it came to health issues.

In 1997, after spending two years in Taiwan, where we'd gotten engaged, Angela and I moved to New York City to attend business school. There, I'd go for long jogs to keep my mind clear and stay in shape (which is why I used to be thin). In 2002, though, I had to stop running; my feet became crippled.

When we first moved to Greenwich Village, I would journey southward along the West Side Highway toward the twin towers of the World Trade Center that jutted from the ground like mountains of ice. After a while, though, I would find myself having to stop mid-run. Numb feet. Burning feet. Painfully tight calves.

Jog, stop, stretch...Jog, stop, stretch...repeat. This happened several times per outing.

Despite the pain, though, I kept jogging, and at one point was training for the New York City Marathon—or at least trying to. One summer afternoon, when the sun had turned the running path along the upper West Side Highway into a broiling waffle iron, I found myself leaning hard with my hands against a steel lamppost bolted to the sidewalk, the sixth lamppost punctuating my effort thus far. Strangers passed by, some trotting, some biking, others rollerblading. Meanwhile, my feet had turned into blocks of wood. They were completely numb. And after a while, they started to burn as if stuck in boiling oil. Yet with each lamppost, I held out hope that stretching would make the pain and numbness disappear so I could keep going. My efforts proved fruitless. I simply couldn't make it more than a hundred yards. The agony was too intense.

Looks like I'm not doing the marathon...

More than that, the prospect of running for any meaningful distance or duration ended forever.

Angela and I moved away from Manhattan a few months later, not because of 9/11, though it unfolded just blocks from where we lived, but because of the cost of living. I was tired of paying a thousand dollars a month in taxes alone for our one-bedroom apartment, on top of yet *another* thousand dollars monthly in property fees. All *in addition* to the mortgage. Plus, there was the four hundred monthly it cost to park my used Honda Accord in a nearby garage.

Discouraged after spending two weekends walking through awkward, old, and unappealing rentals on the opposite side of the Hudson River from NYC in Hoboken, New Jersey, I got a call from my very good friend Steve, another college roommate. He lived south of Hoboken in the ever-so-creatively named Jersey City. Steve told us to come and take a look at a vacant apartment in his building, and after a short tour, we signed a lease and moved onto the floor above them. We couldn't have been happier to land so close to friends (and in a pleasant building!).

Now, the move wasn't without adjustment. If you've never lived for an extended period in Manhattan, this will sound ridiculous and pretentious, but it's true: Manhattan is very provincial. You get so used to the nonstop energy and buzz. The all-night delis. The ubiquitous taxis. The endless variety of restaurants. The freedom to walk anywhere—never a need to drive. Culture, stimulation. Nonstop. It gets to where you have a hard time imagining life anywhere else. New Jersey, as lovely as it is, doesn't quite offer such flavor. It's because of this, for example, that I held onto my New York license plate for as long as I could after we moved out of the city. I gave it up only when the Garden State forced me to use one of theirs.[2]

On our first visit to a Jersey City grocery store, Angela cried. Literally. "There's no fresh produce here," she sobbed. Again, silly? Pretentious? Maybe. But it happened. And I commiserated. Thus began two years of commuting by ferry from a tiny port in Jersey City to the island of Manhattan—Angela to the southern tip of the city, I to the distinctly uncharming midtown—followed by another

---

2   Don't get me wrong. Angela and I loved living in Jersey City. And the state is wonderful.

two years of commuting by PATH, New Jersey's version of the NYC subway system.

Unfortunately, it wasn't long before I couldn't walk from our apartment to the PATH station or ferry without having to stop multiple times to give my feet a chance to escape the burning that would inevitably arise. And the subway offered no relief as it was generally too crowded for me to find an open seat.

Now just walking is an issue?

ENOUGH IS ENOUGH

Angela and I moved from Jersey City to the Seattle area at the end of 2004, when Luke was a year old. At that point, the word "leukemia" had yet to even enter my vocabulary. There, amid the beauty and peace of the Pacific Northwest, the distances I could walk grew shorter and shorter. I couldn't even make my way around the cafeteria at Microsoft, where I had come to work, before having to sit and let my feet recover.

I searched endlessly for a solution. A podiatrist in Sammamish, a suburb located a few miles east of the Microsoft campus, made me (expensive) orthotics. They didn't help, so I traveled to a shabby clinic in the middle of New Jersey where a physician used an experimental method to freeze nerves in my feet. No impact. Nothing changed. After years of doctors, therapists, and surgeries, I almost gave up on finding a fix for the pain. I'd simply come to accept the handicap. Meanwhile, conditions deteriorated further. Not only would my feet sting, but also my calves started to cramp after climbing even a single flight of stairs—something I had to do multiple times a day. And the cramps wouldn't go away. They persisted even after I sat down.

One day, when Luke was two years old (Sofia was yet to be conceived), Angela and I brought him to Discovery Park, a massive expanse located off the shores of Puget Sound. It was a sunny August day, and in the late summer, the grass had already dried into a pale, burnt yellow.

Upon arrival, we embarked on a narrow asphalt path rising gently from the parking lot toward a pine-covered hill. We made our way all of three hundred yards before I had to stop.

"Can we pause here?" I pleaded.

"Feet?" asked Angela.

"Yes. And calves."

We pushed Luke's stroller under a tree, next to a weathered picnic table. Angela unbuckled him and let him clamber toward a nearby playset, which despite his age he navigated like a pro, as he always did such structures. Tiny Luke, climbing, sliding, and running. A fearless little boy maneuvering among the big kids, oblivious to their greater size. As far as Luke was concerned, he was just as big.

"My calves are as tight as rocks," I told Angela.

"Can I help?"

"Maybe. Let's try something." We put Luke back in his stroller and I lay face down on a picnic table so Angela could knead my calves with her sharp elbows...all while park visitors in sun hats passed by, staring.

Despite the punishing shiatsu of Angela's elbows, though, the cramps wouldn't go away.

Enough is enough. This couldn't go on. I went to see Dr. Venazzi the following week.

"How often do you cramp?" she asked.

"My calves used to cramp after a few hundred yards or so. Now they cramp almost immediately—and the cramp *won't go away*. And my feet sting."

"I have an idea," said Dr. Venazzi. "I don't know if it'll help, but I think it's worth visiting a vascular specialist for an ultrasound so we can check the blood flow in your legs."

I had never heard of a vascular specialist, but was willing to give it a try.

"I have one I can recommend," Dr. Venazzi went on.

Not long after that conversation, I found myself lying on my back in a dim examination room at the office of a local vascular surgery practice. It was my first visit to a medical facility named Overlake Hospital in Bellevue—unbeknownst to me, my future home away from home. As I stared at the muted sconces adorning the wall, a young technician poured gel onto the back of my left calf and began sliding a plastic wand across it, pausing intermittently to record images.

Snap!

Snap!

After a good ten minutes, the technician, who looked all of twenty-two, broke the silence. "Dr. Venazzi prescribed an ultrasound of your calves, but I have a suspicion we need to look at more than just your calves. Let me ask Dr. Hills a couple of questions. I'll be right back."

I was answering email on a BlackBerry when she returned.

"OK, I've scanned your calves, and I'm going to run the ultrasound across your inner thighs as well. I want to examine the blood flow in the femoral arteries."

So poised and confident for someone so young. I was impressed.

The young technician placed the wand on the back of my upper-left thigh and proceeded again to slide it slowly across the surface. After finishing with the left thigh, she moved to the right. The room remained dim and silent save for the sound of the snap-snapping.

She stopped. I could tell she'd found something.

"I'll be right back," she said.

When the young technician returned, she was joined by a slight, kind-looking physician with blue eyes that reflected light, energy, and intelligence.

"Mr. Harp?"

"Walt, please."

"I'm Dr. Hills. I'm a vascular surgeon here at Overlake."

"Nice to meet you."

"Let's see if we can figure out what's going on."

Dr. Hills sat on a stool by the exam table and turned to face me. I rose to a seated position so that our eyes were level. Pointing to an image on the monitor, she said, "It looks like you've suffered popliteal aneurysms behind both of your knees." I could see on the screen what looked like a fleshy x-ray of the inside of my left leg, down the middle of which ran a shoestring that rounded behind the knee before forking into branches that led to the calf. I learned that the "shoestring" was the popliteal artery, a continuation of the femoral artery responsible for bringing oxygenated blood from the heart to the lower limbs. At the knee, the artery had blown up into a balloon-sized golf ball.

"How these aneurysms happened, I don't know," Dr. Hills went on. "It's very, very rare to see popliteal aneurysms in someone so young. Has anyone in your family had these?"

"No..."

"Well, blood clots have been forming and collecting in the aneurysms behind your knees for several years now, it seems. Over time they have hardened and chipped off into sediment that has since shot down into the smaller vessels and capillaries below your knees, essentially filling them with the equivalent of organic sand. Blood can barely reach the calves, much less the feet, which is why you've been suffering pain when you walk."

In medical terms:

An aneurysm is a swelling of an artery. A popliteal aneurysm is a swelling of the popliteal artery. The popliteal artery extends across the lower third of the thigh and the upper third of the calf. It is situated quite deeply in the leg behind the knee. These aneurysms are relatively uncommon. Most patients (95 percent) are elderly men with a median age of about 71 years. We do not know exactly why popliteal aneurysms develop.

The main risk from a popliteal aneurysm is related to embolization...fragments of clot become jammed in the arteries obstructing blood flow to the tissues downstream.

Sometimes popliteal aneurysms can suddenly block off and obstruct blood flow to the lower leg and foot. In some patients this will happen and the leg will remain alive and viable. The only symptom these patients notice is pain in the calf muscles on walking. On other occasions this acute blockage can cause severe ischemia (shortage of blood) resulting in a threatened limb which if not successfully treated within 6-12 hours will require amputation. The chances of success when treating an aneurysm will be strongly influenced by how much of the arterial tree downstream is open with

*blood flowing and how much is obstructed by
old clot.*[3]

I was absolutely thrilled that Dr. Hills had solved the
mystery. *Thrilled.* More precisely, I was grateful that the
young technician had followed her instinct to go beyond
what was prescribed. I was so, so lucky.

"You need a femoral bypass in both legs," Dr. Hills
continued. "We need to give blood a new route to get from
your thighs to your calves and feet or else they're going to
run out of oxygen."

"When do we need to do *that*?"

"The sooner the better." We scheduled surgery for the
following week.

A few days later, Angela was sitting in a blue upholstered
chair in the carpeted waiting area adjacent to the
operating room at Overlake while I underwent the two
femoral bypasses. The procedures were supposed to take
two hours in total, but it was actually eight hours later that
Dr. Hills materialized in the waiting room, still wearing
scrubs.

"I was able to save both feet," she told Angela.

Save the feet?! Neither of us had had any idea what was
at stake...

"I was able to use a single vein on the right leg to create

---

3   Source: www.vascular.co.nz.

a bypass," Dr. Hills explained. "The left leg, though, was far worse than I expected. I had to harvest three pieces of vein and stitch them together to create a graft of sufficient length."

Once I was home, the resulting discomfort from the long incisions running down my groin and legs limited my ability to shuffle about the house to mere inches at a time. I'd place my hand on the wall to keep stable, wincing with every step. After a few days, though, I gained enough mobility to return to work, where I could make my way between my office, nearby conference rooms, and the men's bathroom—everything I needed was within fifty feet or so.

After I had fully recovered, I noticed that the bottoms of my feet no longer burned when I walked! Sure, my calves still cramped if I journeyed more than a couple hundred yards—and, of course, I still couldn't jog—but I could tell things were better. The bypasses had improved the flow of oxygen below my knees substantially.

Grinning, I looked Luke straight in the eye and said, "Take it out."[4]

A couple of months had passed since the bypass surgery with Dr. Hills, and Luke and I were playing basketball in the cul-de-sac in front of our house. At age three, Luke

---

4   In half-court basketball, a player must take the ball outside the top of the three-point line to initiate play after an opponent has scored.

stood barely higher than the ball. I shuffled back to guard him and let him dribble past me, which he did using both hands. I lifted him to the rim so he could make a basket.

"Nice!" I called out. "Now my turn."

I dribbled the ball to the top of our makeshift half court, Luke trailing behind. I bounced the orange sphere to him so he could "check it," and he bounced it back. As I pushed off the ground with my left foot to head to the basket, though, I felt numbness. Something was clearly wrong.

"The bypass in the left leg has collapsed," explained Dr. Hills in her office the next day. "I need to go back in."

"When?"

"Now. If we don't act immediately, the graft may not open again."

I called Angela right from Dr. Hills' exam room to let her know I was being admitted and asked her to bring an overnight bag. "You're not going to believe this..."

As it turned out, one of the three pieces of vein Dr. Hills had sewn together to make the graft in my left leg had clogged. So she harvested yet another piece of healthy vein from elsewhere in my leg and swapped it in for the damaged segment. And once again I went back to two weeks of hobbling and wincing, bummed because the incident kept me from attending a scheduled meeting with Microsoft CEO Steve Ballmer, where the discussion was to include a project I was leading.

Frustrating.

A month or so later, Dr. Hills took me to the basement of Overlake Hospital's North Tower. There, she placed a translucent image of the inside of my leg in all of its cardiovascular glory against a wall of backlit glass. On the ultrasound she had circled in red the segment of the graft that she had replaced.

"Unlike most of the people who get grafts in later years, you're still young and healthy, so this section of the graft, the one I've circled, is trying to heal itself by building scar tissue. And it's the scar tissue that blocked the graft the last time and that will inevitably block it again. The difficult part is that we've run out of suitable veins in your leg from which to create a new graft once this one fails. The only other place I could harvest more veins at this point would be in your arms, although even those veins may be too narrow.

We're not pulling veins from my arms.

"There's no other option?" I asked while staring at the glowing image on the wall, a pit in my stomach.

"We could use a synthetic graft, but they don't last long."

Shit. This isn't good.

Despite the growing threat, the graft managed to stay open...at least for a couple of years, until it competed with an entirely new malady: leukemia. Then I would have to choose between saving my left foot and getting chemo to save my life.

Above Left: Young and carefree in Iowa (1989).

Above Right: Standing across the Hudson from our former home, Manhattan (2001).

Bottom: Family hike in the Pacific Northwest (August 2008). The bypasses in my legs were working fine and the word leukemia had yet to cross my mind.

PRESIDENTIAL ELECTION

"Is that a Spiderman outfit?"

"Yeah, right, Dad," Luke, now just days from turning five years old, retorted, wearing his Batman pajamas—black cape and all—as he stood on a stool so he could reach the top of the kitchen island.

"I dunno...looks like Spiderman to me!"

"Well...you look like Chewbacca!"

"Funny you should say that. I saw Chewbacca at your school yesterday."

"Really?"

"Yup—and Darth Vader, too."

Accustomed to my endless teasing, Luke ignored me.

"Dad?" he then asked.

"What?"

"You know who this is?" He pointed to the Lego figure he was assembling, a futuristic warrior with swords of fire in each hand.

"Um...you?"

"No. It's Tahu."

"Is that like a Barbie?"

"He's a Bionicle!"

Luke could plow through Lego sets in fifteen minutes or

less and be ready to move on to the next. He must have inherited his grandfathers' engineering brains because the kits never presented a challenge. One of Luke's grandfathers held a PhD in electrical engineering and was a lead scientist for over twenty years at IBM Watson Research. The other was a chemical engineer who went on to work for Exxon, Frito-Lay, and Kroger.

I was pretty sure I was going to go bankrupt buying Legos.

"Hey, sweetheart...give Daddy a kissy." I picked up my laptop bag and walked around the island to collect my kiss on the cheek, which even today, eight years later, I still get whenever one of us leaves the house, even though Luke is twelve. I'm waiting for the shoe to drop—for that day when he's too old to give his Dad kissies. I'm not at what age that happens. Maybe it doesn't. Who knows? My parents never did the kissy thing.

The air was cold later that night when Angela and I walked out of the large white church where we had cast our ballots in the 2008 presidential election. Mist filtered the light as it cascaded from the streetlamps, creating a soft, glowing shower beneath each one.

"Should we grab dinner?" I asked.

"Sure—where?"

"There's a little Italian restaurant at the bottom of the hill."

"Sounds good."

Angela and I had driven separately to the church after work, so we left our two cars parked on a side street and made our way in silence toward a narrow stretch of road lined with quaint stores and boutique restaurants known as Old Bellevue. There we sat down to light and tasty bowls of fresh ravioli accompanied by what, in my nonexpert opinion, seemed a nice Chianti. An unexpected moment of romance. Not easy to come by when you're busy with two small children and two demanding jobs.

"You hear that?" I asked.

"What?"

"Obama is winning."

"How do you know?"

"The   staff   in   the   kitchen   is   cheering!"[5] As we walked back to our cars, I could sense the onset of body aches. *I'm getting sick. Should've worn my coat.*

The next day I found myself back in Dr. Venazzi's office sitting on the edge of an exam table, where I was following up on the suggestion from the physician in the ER Halloween night that I see someone about my low platelet count.

"I want you to make an appointment with a hematologist

---

5   Yes, I made a leap. Perhaps they were cheering as states came in for McCain.

I know," said Dr. Venazzi.

A hematologist? Really? Who sees a hematologist?

Yet another doctor's appointment I needed to hassle with.

Or not. I never saw the hematologist. I didn't have a chance before the chaos hit.

I left Dr. Venazzi's and returned to my office at Microsoft's main campus, located a few blocks away. Back at work, I walked into a conference room in Building Red West A, where a dozen or so of my peers were reviewing a new promotional video. As is protocol in an overcrowded Microsoft conference room with no open seats, I shimmied onto the counter covering the trash and recycling receptacles in the back of the room. To my surprise, the simple act left me winded.

That's odd...

"This video isn't realistic," Jennifer, a friend from the online advertising group, called out unexpectedly. "Our products have ads in them. This video doesn't show *any* ads."

"Why would it show ads?" I responded a bit testily. *Why am I irritated?*

"You don't understand our side of the business," Jennifer retorted. "Advertisers want to see where the placements are!"

Jennifer and I went back and forth a couple of times,

succeeding only in getting aggravated. (I apologized afterward. Months later, she told me she knew something was wrong—that my face had turned gray.) The broader discussion resumed, and after listening for a while, I slid off the counter and made my way to the restroom twenty feet outside of the meeting. The walk there and back? It left me winded again.

What was going on?

"I just need to lie down for a bit," I called out to Angela, my arm draped over my closed eyes as I lay face up on the aqua-blue microfiber couch in our living room that night. Meanwhile, miles away a taxi was winding a path to our house to take me to Sea-Tac Airport for a late flight to San Jose. Despite Angela's foreboding, I was set on attending the product meetings with our engineering team in Mountain View, California, scheduled for the next two days.

Angela, annoyed at my intransigence, scolded me. "You should stay home—you're sick."

Ten times out of ten, she's right.

"Just need five minutes," I countered, my eyes still closed. Then my cell phone rang. It was an automated recording from FarWest Taxi announcing that my ride had arrived—an actual yellow cab, not a black Prius or SUV (this was still well before Uber). So I dragged myself off the couch, grabbed my laptop bag and suitcase, gave Angela a kiss, and left for the airport.

"Hey, guys!"

One of the product managers on my team, Irene, a driven, highly intelligent, yet mild-mannered woman in her late twenties, was already seated at the gate along with Arshad, one of our team's product planners. We were all headed to Mountain View.

"Hi, Walt!" both Arshad and Irene replied.

"You guys heading to San Jose?" I asked, somewhat rhetorically.

"Yes," Arshad replied, "Want to carpool when we get there?"

"Sure—that'd be great. Where are you staying?"

"Hotel Avante."

"Hah! I'm there, too. Irene?"

"My parents are picking me up. I'm staying with them."

OK—Arshad and me to the Avante, Irene with her parents.

The three of us chatted for a bit but I soon became fatigued. I wanted to lie down. And my body ached.

Probably just the flu.

"I'm not feeling that great, guys," I confessed. "I'm going to find a place to rest until it's time to board."

"Of course, no problem," Irene and Arshad replied almost in unison.

Once on the plane, I propped my head against the

oval window shade and slept the full two hours to San Jose. Though I opened my eyes a couple of times during the flight, I wasn't conscious until we pulled into the arrival gate, and even then I was only half awake. Once the plane rolled to a stop and the overhead bell dinged, I disembarked in single file along with the rest of the passengers and found Arshad waiting for me at the end of the exit ramp. We hopped a shuttle bus to the Avis lot, where the Avis Preferred leaderboard featured Arshad's last name in yellow letters. We climbed inside a maroon Pontiac Grand Am to head to the Hotel Avante. I stared ahead, preoccupied with my malaise, as Arshad stopped to show his license and rental contract at the exit gate before driving us out of the lot.

"I need to sleep," I said to no one in particular.

"What's the matter?" Arshad asked.

"I'm getting sick."

"I've got exactly the thing for you. It cures *everything*. I use it all the time."

"Yeah?"

I dismissed Arshad's claim as implausible but appreciated his thoughtfulness. "You'll have to give me some when we get to the hotel."

Not long after, as we waited for the elevator in the Hotel Avante's small but stylish lobby, Arshad turned to me. "Take this," he said and with his index finger scooped out a glob of orange mucus-like goo from a canister that reminded me of the snuff cans kids carried in junior high.

"Thanks, man."

Might as well...

I closed my eyes and popped the snot gob into my mouth. It didn't taste like much. Just a flavorless chunk of creamy salve.

Two floors later I said goodnight to Arshad, exited the elevator, swiped the keycard in a door down the hall, and walked into a dark hotel room. I rolled my carry-on into a corner and phoned Angela.

"I made it," I said when she answered. She sounded sleepy, but I could tell she appreciated the call, particularly since I wasn't always good about calling to check in after flights.

SURRENDER

When midnight arrived in Mountain View, I was nowhere near sleep. My back had flared up again, and the pain was even worse than when Angela had taken me to the ER at Overlake. I called down to the Avante's front desk.

"Does the hotel have any pain medicine?" I asked the clerk. I already knew the answer would be no, but with the morning's meetings rapidly approaching, I needed a quick fix and gave it a shot regardless.

"No, we do not keep medication," the clerk replied.

"Well, is there a drugstore nearby?"

"There's a Walgreens on El Camino Real."

"Walking distance?"

"Probably a thirty-minute walk."

"A bit too far. Thanks, though."

I hung up, and the pain simply grew worse.

Tick tock, tick tock.

Tick tock, tick tock.

I considered my options. Arshad had the keys to the rental car, but I didn't want to wake him. There was a Walgreens nearby, but too far to walk. I had to do something—the pain was becoming unbearable.

"Could you please order me a taxi?" I asked the clerk, whom I had called once again.

"Yes, sir. I would be happy to do that."

Minutes later, I rode the elevator three floors to the lobby and walked out to the parking lot where a yellow taxi waited. I told the driver where I was headed, and he set off to the north, motoring for many blocks under street lamps and overpasses before finally pulling into the parking lot in front of the Walgreens, where bright fluorescent light emanated through the windows, beckoning me.

"Can you wait ten minutes?" I asked. "You can keep the meter running."

The garishly mottled aisles of beauty products, Hallmark

cards, and plastic toys caused my head to recoil when the overload of visual signals hit the occipital lobes. Luckily, I found the analgesics fairly easily. Scores of products for muscle and back pain filled the shelves. I picked the biggest Icy Hot patches I could find, grabbed a giant roll of opaque, aqua-blue taffy pain gel strip, took a Thera-Med Maximum Strength Back Pad from a shelf, and tossed it all into the red plastic shopping basket I carried.

Back at the Avante, after I had poured the bag of futility onto the bathroom counter, I removed the thin wrapping from the Thera-Med pad and pasted it across my shoulders. I took three Advil, lay down on the bed, and pulled the thin blanket up to my chin.

Lights off. The numbers on the clock read 2:30 a.m.

My bones continued to pound.

And pound.

And pound.

Not surprisingly, none of the over-the-counter menagerie I had purchased from Walgreens were making a difference. The torment grew intolerable.

Call Angela.

"Ange?" I said into the phone, dehydrated from the late hour.

"Yes?" she answered groggily.

"The pain is back."

"You need to go to the emergency room," came the adamant reply.

"I don't want to. The meetings are tomorrow!" In a few hours, actually—it was already 4 a.m.

"You're not going to any meetings."

Crap. But she was right. Again. No gray area here: I wasn't going to any meetings, so I surrendered and called for another taxi.

Angela: Months later, the attending at the Seattle Cancer Care Alliance would nod his head knowingly when Walt told him about the severe pain he had experienced in his back, shoulder blades, and ribs that night in Silicon Valley. "The pressure of the rapidly expanding mass of leukemic blasts against the inside of your bones was causing the ache," he explained.

Dust hung in the air in the dimly lit lobby of the emergency room at Mountain View's Evergreen Hospital.[6] Drab tiled ceilings hung over a dozen scratched plastic chairs riveted in rows across a featureless, wear-resistant carpet. Through a wall of what seemed like bulletproof glass bordering one side of the room, I spotted a woman sitting with her back to me.

"Excuse me..." I said tentatively.

No response.

---

6   The name has been changed.

"Excuse me…" I said a little louder. The heavyset receptionist pivoted her chair to face me.

"Can I help you?" she asked flatly, her eyes glazed over as if my presence at Evergreen Hospital's emergency room was irritatingly inconvenient.

"I'm in a terrible amount of pain," I told her as objectively as possible but with enough emphasis that I hoped she'd realize the severity.

"I need your ID and insurance card," she replied robotically, so I pulled both from my well-worn black leather wallet and handed them to her through the opening in the glass. She proceeded to enter the information into her computer, making sharp *clacks* on the keyboard with her impressively long, flawlessly manicured blue nails.

Clack, clack, clack.

After several minutes of this, she lifted her head and said, "You can have a seat. Someone will be with you shortly." The dreary Greyhound bus station of a waiting area was abandoned, so I had my choice of chairs.

The wait was torturous. The pain in my bones grew so bad that I began to rock back and forth just as I had in bed a few days earlier. Soon the clock had counted thirty minutes. I rocked harder, despairing. Hair spiked and wild, I tried to mat it down with my hands.

Shit. I probably look like a drug addict sitting here at 4 a.m., rocking back and forth in a chair. They think I'm here to scam them out of pain meds. Fuck. They're not going to help me.

I sported a comfortable yet ratty T-shirt that hung sloppily below the waistline of my well-worn fleece. The Keen sandals on my feet added a splash of Pacific Northwest flair, but I suddenly realized the overall ensemble read "junkie."

A young Latino woman wearing floral scrubs interrupted my thoughts.

"Mr. Harp?" she said loudly, as if my burger order was up.

"Yes?"

"Come with me, please."

I trailed behind her through swinging doors to a small desk, where she motioned me toward the wooden chair next to it.

"What's the problem?" she asked pleasantly enough, though I was certain I detected an edge of skepticism.

She thinks I'm here to scam drugs. "My back hurts. It *really* hurts."

Expressionless, she turned to her PC and started typing.

Clack, clack, clack.

She, too, had exceedingly long nails.

"Where does it hurt exactly?" she asked without looking up.

"Everywhere. My shoulders, my ribs, my hips."

Clack, clack, clack.

"Is the address on your insurance current?"

"Yes." It wasn't, but I wasn't about to introduce complexity into the process.

"Are you currently on any medication?"

"No."

"Are you allergic to any medication?"

"No."

"Do you...?"

"Are there...?"

"What is...?"

I started to rock again. *She thinks I'm an addict.*

"Any surgeries since...?"

"Can we please hurry?" I pleaded, this time starting to break down. "It *really* hurts."

"We're almost done."

Clack, clack, clack. Clack, clack, clack.

"Now let's weigh you."

Peeking through a crack in the tall blue curtains that enclosed my bed, I could see that mine wasn't the only blue teepee. It was one among several in a village, from which echoed the hushed voices of nurses and patients punctuated with an occasional soft moan.

Without warning, one of the nurses ripped open the curtains to my domicile and said nothing as she briskly stepped inside, turned, and yanked them shut. She walked to the head of my bed, sat on a stool inches from my face, and set an IV kit on a small table. Pulling my right hand to her lap, she turned it backside-up and started to percuss it as if testing a cantaloupe for ripeness. She was hunting for veins, several of which weaved about the metacarpals under the skin. No fat. Just skin, bone, and veins. This was going to hurt.

Tap tap...pause...

The nurse mulled her options.

Tap tap...pause...

Unwrapping the IV kit, she took hold of the needle and poked it into the back of my hand and waited to see if blood would backflow. Which it didn't. It was a miss.

Brow furrowed, the nurse swiveled the needle underneath the skin to see if a different angle would make a difference. It didn't. It only succeeded in sparking nerve endings.

The nurse poked my hand four more times, each time pulling the needle out, driving it back in, and swiveling it left to right before she finally struck oil and left the tent with three small vials of my blood in her hand.

She returned with a syringe of clear liquid. Either

they had determined I wasn't an addict or didn't care.[7]

Not much time passed before another woman opened the entrance to the tent. Because of the backlighting, all I could make out was her silhouette.

"We can't let you leave," said the woman. "Your platelet count is eight thousand."

I had no idea what the number meant, but she sounded serious. Little did I know that by that point leukemic blasts had destroyed almost the entirety of platelets in my blood. Eight thousand platelets per milliliter of blood is far lower than the normal range of 150,000 to 450,000. In fact, it's pretty well on its way to zero.

Nothing she said alarmed me.

When I awoke not long after that encounter, I couldn't help but notice how starkly the black sock on my right foot contrasted against the white sheet that shrouded me on the gurney where I lay. Hazy from the pain medication— whatever it was—I looked around and discovered that someone had rolled me into an office. Books and papers were draped from shelves onto a dove-colored Formica desk that spanned the wall. I still wore my street clothes— black socks, jeans, T-shirt, fleece—instead of a hospital. I'd

---

7   I have a photo taken a few days after my fuss with the nurse. My right arm, from wrist to shoulder, is purple and yellow. With almost no platelets in my body, I bruised easily from all the poking in my hand.

been triaged "as is" into a back room.

My first inclination? I needed to let Arshad know I wasn't going to make the meetings since we had planned to drive together. He could tell the others what had happened. So I reached with my right hand to pull the flip phone from my front pocket and dialed.

"Hello?" Arshad answered. It was obvious I'd awakened him.

"Hey. It's Walt."

"Hey. What's up?"

"I had to go to the emergency room last night."

"*What*?"

"I'm not going to make the meetings this morning. Can you let everyone know?"

"What happened?"

"My back flared up. They say I can't leave."

"How did you get to the hospital?"

"I took a taxi."

"Why didn't you ask me to take you?" I could tell by the inflection of his voice that his feelings were hurt.

"I didn't want to wake you."

"Dude, I could have taken you, no problem."

Learning moment.

US SENATE, HART OFFICE BUILDING, WASHINGTON, DC, JULY 1993

"Good morning! I'm here for our mail!" Angela exclaimed, smiling as she entered the far end of the mailroom or, to be more exact, mail cove. As always, the space brightened.

"But of course," I replied, bowing.

It was 1993, the year Angela and I met. Bill Clinton had just kicked off his first year in office and, having just passed into law the Don't Ask, Don't Tell policy, was now pushing health care reform legislation, an initiative spearheaded by his wife, Hillary. Meanwhile, Angela and I were both working for starvation wages as low-level staffers for the same US Senator on Capitol Hill. I had no car, but I could afford the Metro—and rent for a room in a house I shared with an eclectic group of people, including the waitress I had worked with when I first got to DC as an intern.

"This place is a pigsty. You need to clean it up," Angela teased.

"I don't know what you're talking about—it is pristine."

I walked over to the cubby holding mail for the Subcommittee on Disability Policy—Angela's outfit—grabbed the multicolored stack of envelopes, and handed them to her.

"I've got some news," I announced.

"Yeah? What is it?"

"I've been promoted."

"Really? Congratulations! To what?"

"Legislative Correspondent."

"LC? You're not the mailroom guy anymore?"

"Nope. LC."

Angela's eyes widened. "I was trying for that job! I'm so pissed at you!"

"Seniority."

I had been there longer. That's all.

I didn't realize it at the time, but Angela's twice-daily visits to the mailroom were uplifting. And there was chemistry.

I should ask her out—do it!

I dialed the Subcommittee office.

"Angela? It's Walt."

"Hey!"

"I have tickets to the National Holocaust Museum. Wanna go?" As weird as it sounds, it was actually a "thing" to have tickets to the National Holocaust Museum. It had just opened to a lot of buzz and tickets were very hard to come by. I didn't see anything wrong with the proposal.

"Um..." Angela hesitated. It wasn't the most romantic venue. "I don't think I can make it. Maybe another time?" So instead we went to see *The Paper*—an awful movie by Ron Howard—joined by Melissa, one of Angela's close friends from college and one of her housemates. We still laugh that our first date was chaperoned.

A few dates later, including two on which Angela cooked me what I later discovered were the only two recipes she actually knew how to make, we stood in the middle of the lamplit street outside the red brick apartment building where she lived in DuPont Circle. We'd just met another couple—Angela's best friend from high school and her longtime boyfriend (the two later married)—which was the status equivalent of meeting the in-laws. Apparently I passed. Angela said goodnight, then, standing on her toes, kissed me on the cheek and ran inside.

EVERGREEN HOSPITAL, MOUNTAIN VIEW, CALIFORNIA, NOVEMBER 6, 2008

Fluorescent lights and stale ceiling tiles scrolled overhead as an orderly rushed me on a gurney through a corridor in the basement of Evergreen. Having spoken with Arshad only minutes before, I was now in a gown and giddy from the gallons of pain medication. The orderly soon pushed me into a small, dark room where a technician sat staring at a glowing monitor.

"I'm going to take a few pictures of your chest and abdomen," she said as she squeezed cold gel onto my chest and placed what felt like the back of a hairbrush on top of it. She began sliding the sensor slowly across my torso, pausing every inch or so to capture an image.

Then it was back to the corridor, the aged ceiling tiles

once again rolling top to bottom across my line of vision like the frames of an old movie reel, until we turned left into another room, one far brighter than the ultrasound lab. "Welcome!" cracked a boisterous voice. I turned my head to find a young Asian man in silver glasses, his thick black hair parted neatly on the side, smiling at me as he stood by my gurney.

How can he possibly be so enthusiastic doing the same thing every day down here in the basement?

He sent me through the CT scan, in and out in seconds, before the orderly rushed me away. Back in my room, the chaos still buzzing in my head, a nurse informed me that Angela was on the phone.

"Ange?"

"What happened?"

"I went to the emergency room last night. They still have me here, and can't let me leave because my platelet count is so low. You need to come down. I need you to get my luggage from the hotel." Euphoric from the pain medication, I expressed more concern about the luggage than anything else.

Angela immediately canceled Luke's fifth birthday party, scheduled for the following day, jumped on a plane to San Jose, and came straight to my room from the airport. The moment I saw her, the chaos settled. But only for a brief moment. Then the volume went back up. Too much stimulation.

Angela: Walt's phone call that morning was one of the most surreal moments of my life. Having suffered a stroke at the age of twelve, I had always been the one with health issues, and he had been the one I'd relied on for strength. I felt horror but quickly pushed that feeling down and shifted to hyperdrive. I needed to take action, which included finding coverage for the kids.

When I called Walt back, the nurse who answered the phone said, "Mr. Harp can't come to the phone right now, he's having tests done." And then she casually added, "Things are serious. They think he has leukemia." I didn't break down. I didn't have time. Too many logistics.

Walking down the neon-lit causeway to the gate at SeaTac, though, the dam broke. I called my best friend, Carey, back in New York and wept as the adrenaline drained.

When the tests came back from nearby Stanford University Medical Center, they indeed showed positive for leukemia. And honestly, I felt nothing. I had no idea of the repercussions. I didn't even know what leukemia was. And with so many opioids in my system, I was impervious to concern.

On learning the diagnosis, the doctor assigned to me suggested I stay at Evergreen for treatment rather than return to Seattle, which even amid the bedlam felt a little odd—yet at the same time made sense. Maybe he didn't see many patients like me, I reasoned. Maybe this was an opportunity for him. He was bored and wanted a challenge. Intoxicated, I'd become bar buddies with the man, so the idea of remaining with him carried some appeal. Even Angela gave it brief consideration (yes—moving to California rather than going home to Seattle for care). Thankfully, my wife made the wise choice to call the hematologist she knew back in Bellevue. Placing the phone on my bed, she set it to speaker and dialed. The voice that answered? *Authority.* It was a Dr. Tanya Austin, who took charge from hundreds of miles away and without the slightest waver ordered Angela and me to return to Seattle for chemo. Immediately.

No more nonsense.

Angela: Dr. Austin had cared for me during my pregnancy with Sofia. In contrast to the doctors on the maternity ward when I gave birth to Luke, Dr. Austin got me an epidural (thank God). She didn't agree there existed the risk the others had perceived given my history of stroke. And as it turned out, Dr. Austin was not only a hematologist, which is why I had gone to her, but she was a hematology-oncologist. A blood cancer specialist. Hello?

After we'd hung up with Dr. Austin, Angela phoned her cousin, Xiao Long (translation: "Little Dragon," a Chinese pet name equivalent to "little buddy" in English, although Xiao Long at age thirty was anything but little) and her Aunt Elizabeth, both of whom lived nearby and without the slightest hesitation offered to help. Quiet and reserved, Xiao Long arrived with his wife, Tiffany, her face one of the few images I recall from the car ride between Evergreen Hospital and San Jose Airport.

When we arrived at the departure terminal, Xiao Long asked Angela if she wanted help getting me to the gate. Believing an airport courier could do the job, Angela politely declined.

Angela: I had a moment of panic in the middle of the airport when I realized the courier wasn't going to take us where we needed to go and we could be stuck. I don't have full use of my left side, so I didn't have the strength to move the wheelchair on my own. Meanwhile, Walt was pickled. Somehow, though—I don't remember how—I got us to the gate.

Before we boarded the plane, Angela called Kevin, one of my best friends and a former roommate at Stanford, who lived in Seattle at the time, to ask if he could pick us up at Sea-Tac. Kevin kindly agreed, and off we went to the Emerald City. (Seriously—that's Seattle's nickname. Same as the capital of Oz.)

It was ten o'clock and night had long since fallen when we climbed into Kevin's car and began the twenty-minute drive northward on I-5 toward Seattle. En route, I called the one medical professional on the planet I knew who had anything to do with cancer (this was all very new).

Once married to a dear friend of mine, he was—and is—a radiation oncologist.

"Seth?" I asked when he answered the phone.

"Yes?"

"It's Walter," I slurred.

"Oh, hey, Walt! How are you?"

"Not so well."

"What's the matter?"

"I need your help."

"Yes? What is it?"

"I've been told I have leukemia."

"What? That's terrible!" he replied, clearly taken aback. "I'm so sorry! Where are you going for treatment?"

"We're headed to Overlake Hospital in Bellevue."

Seth's reply was sharp and directive. "You need to go to the University of Washington. It's associated with the Hutch."[8]

"We're going to Overlake…"

"Don't go to a private hospital. Go where they're doing research—the Hutch or a university. You'll get the latest treatment that way."

I pulled the phone away from my ear and announced to

---

8   He was referring to the Fred Hutchinson Cancer Research Cancer, where bone marrow transplants were essentially invented.

the car, "Seth says we should go to the Hutch."

"There's already a room waiting for you at Overlake," Angela replied firmly. "Dr. Austin is expecting us."

"We should go to the Hutch."

Angela: Even in his delirium, Walt was insanely logical and grounded in rationality, as is his norm. He wanted to go to the place the expert was recommending even though we knew nothing about it. I, on the other hand, was drawn to the comfort and safety of the known and the familiar—Dr. Austin and Overlake. Such tension is common between us. Walt's more of a calculated risk-taker than I am. It's actually part of the reason we're together. We balance each other out.

I was determined to follow Seth's advice, and none of us really knew any better. So Kevin was soon pulling off of the interstate at the Mercer Street exit north of downtown Seattle and driving in a broad arc toward a cluster of red brick buildings, the Hutch. Not a single light was on. We pulled into its empty driveway at 11 p.m. No one was at work save for the night guard. The Hutch is a research facility, not a hospital or clinic. There's no patient care there. Of course they were closed.

Back to Plan A. Overlake and Dr. Austin. On the way, I tried calling my manager at Microsoft and ended up speaking with his wife. "Tell Roger I have lymphoma," I said, a statement I later corrected in a second call after Angela reminded me it was leukemia.

Angela: Concerned that Walt would make an ass out of himself, I tried to take the phone out of his hands. He of course refused to let go.

As it turned out, I had a particularly nasty form of leukemia: acute lymphoblastic leukemia, or ALL (pronounced A-L-L), as most refer to it. In the US, only 6,600 people are diagnosed with ALL annually, 60 percent of whom are children.[9] No one knows what causes ALL: it just happens. All it takes is for one of the gazillion immature white blood cells in your body—*just one!*—to blow its circuitry and start replicating madly like a rabbit crazed on Viagra. That one tiny little hiccup triggers rapid onset blood cancer that in many cases leads to death—at least for older adults; children have a high cure rate.[10]

---

9   From www.cancer.org: "The American Cancer Society's estimates for acute lymphocytic leukemia (another term for acute lymphoblastic leukemia) in the United States for 2016 (including both children and adults) are:

- About 6,590 new cases of ALL (3,590 in males and 3,000 in females)

- About 1,430 deaths from ALL (800 in males and 630 in females)

The risk for developing ALL is highest in children younger than 5 years of age. The risk then declines slowly until the mid-20s, and begins to rise again slowly after age 50. Overall, about 4 of every 10 cases of ALL are in adults.

Most cases of ALL occur in children, but most deaths from ALL (about 4 out of 5) occur in adults. Children may do better because of differences in childhood and adult ALL in the disease itself, differences in treatment (children's bodies can often handle aggressive treatment better than adults'), or some combination of these.

10   Parents, please don't let me throw you off. I recently read that survival rates are as high as 90 percent for small children diagnosed with ALL. I was thirty-eight years old at diagnosis.

By the time I landed in Seattle, the mutant blood cells—the leukemic blasts—had crowded out all but *ten percent* of the entire population of healthy white blood cells in my body. The rest—90 *percent of my white blood cells*—were now mutant blasts, useless against infection! Imagine—your entire immune system suddenly and completely gone, replaced by malicious, marauding zombie cells multiplying by the millions, each one intent on killing you from the inside out.

And of course my platelets were now approaching nil. It was a wonder I hadn't hemorrhaged and bled out.

Above: Angela and I in our apartment-in-sin in Taipei in 2006, the year we got engaged while on a trip to Bali.

Below: Angela and I in Seattle in 2006, post-femoral bypasses, pre-leukemia.

BALI, INDONESIA, SPRING 1997

In 1995, Angela moved across the world from Washington, DC, to the bustling city of Taipei, Taiwan. We'd tired of Capitol Hill. The mailroom wasn't cutting it, nor was letter-writing. And I couldn't see myself as a lifer on the Hill.[11] So it was goodbye C-SPAN, hello local Taiwanese talk shows, not a word of which I understood—at least on arrival.

Angela and I shared a two-bedroom apartment near one of Taipei's larger universities—one bedroom for sleeping, the other for keeping up the front that Angela and I weren't, um, shacking up, if you will. We did this out of respect for her parents, who also lived in Taiwan at the time (they'd moved back there for a few years after Angela's father retired from IBM). Now, *of course* they knew we were full of bull with the whole two bed thing, particularly since the second bed was always stacked high with laundry. It couldn't have been more obvious I wasn't sleeping there. But in keeping with Chinese-Victorian decorum, no one ever said anything.

While living in Taipei, I proposed to Angela on a trip we took to Bali, Indonesia, in 1997. I'd planned to pop the question atop one of Taipei's taller buildings, but as we sat under the torchlight on the porch of our bungalow near

---

11   Not that working as a staffer on Capitol Hill is a bad thing. Quite the opposite. Despite the bad rap Congress gets—and often, if not mostly, deserves—I worked with some amazing, dedicated people there. Honest, highly intelligent, well-intended, hard-working, salt of the earth.

the Indian Ocean, the time seemed right. And the two Mai Tais we drank only encouraged things.

My mother had given me the engagement ring she received when she married my father (they had long since divorced). It was a tiny thing, but served its purpose, particularly since I had no money to afford another.

Ever the romantic, I made an unforgettable proposal.

"Think we should get married?"

OVERLAKE HOSPITAL, BELLEVUE, WA, NOVEMBER 7, 2008

The fourth floor of Overlake, the cancer ward, was oddly busy given that it was already past midnight when Kevin, Angela, and I arrived after our misguided detour to the Hutch. Nurses stood at PC stations typing in data while others bustled about. Once we were ensconced in my room, Kevin did what any good friend would under similar circumstances: he started filming, recording for posterity my crazily blown-up hair and incessant drug-induced monologues. I think the video may still be on YouTube somewhere.[12]

The next morning, Dr. Austin stepped briskly into the room, her white lab coat billowing, and perched on the aluminum chair next to my bed. With a kind yet

---

12   Actually, it is: http://bit.ly/2elcLGz

authoritative voice and intense blue eyes that didn't seem to blink, she spoke at a rapid clip, reeling off strings of medical terms, drug names, and acronyms I wasn't at all familiar with. cyclophosphamide, mesna, doxorubicin, vincristine, dexamethasone, CBC, WBC...I did my best to take notes in a black spiral notebook Angela had brought me. Hesitant to interrupt the doctor, I spelled everything phonetically to later look up online (Google and Wikipedia are truly your friends for this). I also scribbled down the amounts of each chemo agent I'd be receiving. A liter of this, five hundred milliliters of that, *foo, fee, fah...*

"You're going to be in the hospital for about a week," Dr. Austin explained. I hadn't yet by any stretch grasped the gravity of my situation. I was just following along. Leukemia held no meaning for me, so I didn't think twice about a week of chemo. *Whatever.* Really.

Dr. Austin kicked things off by having Overlake's interventional radiology team insert a "Hickman line" into my chest, a device aptly named for its creator, Dr. Robert Hickman, a brilliant research physician at the Hutch in the 1970s. Before the Hickman line, the only way to administer chemo was for medical staff to jam IV line after IV line into the veins of a patient's arm, meaning an endless number of painful pokes. And chemo administered directly into the veins like that over time would burn them out. Ruined, scorched earth. A Hickman line alleviates all that. It's basically a long plastic tube that enters the chest through a tiny incision made above the collarbone that tunnels through the jugular into the vena cava, right at the return gate to the heart. Once in place, the Hickman provides a "permanent" and convenient way to pipe chemo into a patient's blood system. No more endless succession of pokes and charred veins. (Thank you, Dr. Hickman!) Once my Hickman was in place,[13] it was time

---

13   Because the Hickman hung down my front I could no longer sleep on my stomach, which was my habit. It felt uncomfortable to lie with the Hickman lines pressed between my chest and the mattress. Plus, there was the ongoing concern I might snag the Hickman on a blanket while rolling over in my sleep and thus yank it out (although perhaps in reality, that's not possible). So I capitulated and slept on my back.

Each morning over the months following the Hickman's insertion, when I awoke and stood up from the bed the first thing I noticed was the weight of the tubes and end-caps tugging at the hole in my chest, and I was reminded that I was sick.

The Hickman demanded great care. Twice a day at minimum:

1.   Sit on the toilet, lid down. Sanitize my hands for at least fifteen seconds so that they would be free of bacteria when handling the tubing.

2.   From the cardboard box in the closet, remove four pencil-length syringes, each wrapped in plastic—two with yellow plastic caps at the end signaling that they contained blood thinner, others with white caps indicating saline.

3.   Select one of the syringes. Unscrew the end caps and wipe them with alcohol (careful not to touch them with my fingers; otherwise I'd have to wipe them with alcohol again, having created a risk of bacteria entering the tubes).

4.   Connect the syringes one at a time to the end caps. Push the liquid inside, each time sending a cool sensation to my heart while bringing the taste of peroxide to my mouth.

5.   Once again, wipe everything with alcohol wipes.

The Hickman was a blessing and I was more than grateful for its benefits. Yet its presence demanded months of constant care and vigilance, prevented me from swimming with my kids at the pool or taking a normal shower, and generally hung like an albatross from the clip on the nylon string around my neck that I never removed. The ever-buzzing reminder that my old life was gone did grow tiresome.

to kick off a chemo regimen called Hyper-CVAD (*hyper SEE vad*), the recipe for which went something like this: [14]

- Cyclophosphamide (Cytoxan), an alkylating agent given at 300 mg/m2 by IV Q12hours over 3 hours (6 doses): Days 1, 2, and 3

- Vincristine (Oncovin), a mitotic inhibitor, 2 mg by IV: Days 4 and 11

- Doxorubicin (Adriamycin or Rubex), an antibiotic with anti-tumor effects, 50 mg/m^2 by IV: Day 4

- Dexamethasone (Decadron), an immunosuppressant, 40 mg/day by IV or PO: Days 1–4 and 11–14

- Cytarabine or Ara-C (Cytosar), an antimetabolite, 70 mg IT: Day 7

- Mesna (Uromitexan), a compound used to reduce the incidence of hemorrhagic cystitis, a common side effect of the administration of cyclophosphamide; generally given via intravenous infusion or orally at the same time as cyclophosphamide

- Methotrexate, an antimetabolite, may be given via the intrathecal route when it is necessary to give chemotherapy which will pass through the blood–brain barrier, 12 mg IT: Day 2

This was just Course A (yes, as in dinner course). Course B called for yet another lineup of cell killers and organ protectors.

I celebrated the day when nearly a year post-diagnosis, the hospital finally took the Hickman out. With the tube gone and the portal into my heart closed, my body finally resumed its natural human form.

14   http://en.wikipedia.org/wiki/Hyper-CVAD#Course_A

Moments after the Hickman was in place, a nurse in a mauve tunic breezed into my room carrying the inaugural bag of chemo—the first of many. Housed in a long, clear plastic stocking, the 300 milliliters of liquid, almost the same amount of fluid as in a twelve-ounce can of Coke, was cyclophosphamide (brand name Cytoxan). Literal translation? Cell killer.[15] The urine-colored concoction looked intimidating. Nurses had to wear gloves to handle it.

Around the clock, practiced nurses ferried in bag after bag of chemo and organ protectors, some the size of airplane head pillows, others the size of a deck of playing cards. They hung each one from the tall silver pole next to my bed, grasped by a plastic gray pump similar to how a Koala holds a tree trunk. The pump pushed chemo into my bloodstream via the Hickman at a digitally prescribed pace.

Unlike when I was careening through Evergreen Hospital in Mountain View, I was now sober, so my normal vigilance returned. I carefully recorded each infusion—name, time, and volume. That way I could rest assured that I was receiving the right chemo at the right time and that the nurses didn't miss anything. Not that I needed to do that— they managed the infusions like clockwork, and I soon

15   Bing Dictionary: definition of cytotoxic (adj) [sitō tóksik]

1.   preventing cell division: describes a drug that prevents cell division

2.   killing cells: describes a type of cell in the immune system that destroys other cells

stopped tracking.

There was one and only one goal for this first round of "induction chemo," as it was called, and that was to destroy every single one of the leukemic blasts in my blood within thirty days. To put me into "remission." Leukemia that doesn't succumb to chemo in the first thirty days is considered "refractory" and gives the patient a poor prognosis. That I didn't want.

Walter's Bedside Blog[16]

Leukemia, Day 5 / Chemo, Day 3

Posted by Angela Lean on Wednesday 12/12/08

D'ette [our nanny] brought Luke and Bubble in to see Walt yesterday, and we felt like family "normal" again. I watched with glee as Luke and Walt bantered back and forth about Star Wars and Spiderman (Walt explained that, with his radioactive medicine, if he got bitten by a spider he would indeed become Spiderman). Bubble [Sofia] hopped down the hall, hollering "Daddy, come on, come on!" The kids were reassured by seeing their father, and I literally heard Luke light up with joy later in the evening when asked over the

---

16   A blog set up by my friend Kevin at www.lotsahelpinghands.com

phone whether he was happy to see his dad.

Walt's oncologist was extremely positive about how well Walt has done during this first round of chemo—he may even get a short furlough home if he continues to do so well!

I am amazed by my husband's incredible stamina and will as he endures all of this. He is my inspiration, and I am continually reminded through his humor and grace under fire as to why he is the one for me, my own superhero.

The whole experience continues to be surreal and uncertain. It's only beginning to dawn on me how much this is going to become our true test and what a long road it will be. I know that if anyone has the drive and strength to beat this thing, it's my husband, but, man, this is one scary tunnel to be driving down right now, and we are both desperately hanging on, trying to steer.

I am humbled by the outpouring of love and support from our family, friends, and colleagues. It goes without saying that we would not be getting through this without your support. I am grateful to each and every one of you.

- Angela

HOME

After a relatively uneventful week of Hyper-CVAD at Overlake, I was discharged from by hospital by Dr. Austin, and Angela picked me up in our silver Subaru Forester, complete with the familiar smell of the food and spoiled milk spilled by our small children in the backseat. It also, of course, carried the musky odor of our two dogs, a pug and a Frenchie, the latter of whom vomited during any car trip over one hour in length (much to the chagrin of the pug, who shared a travel crate with her). Even though I felt like I had spent a week drinking Windex, I wasn't queasy, so the car's stink didn't bother me.

Angela pulled into the driveway of our brown 1973 split-level home. Our garage was too stuffed to actually fit a car, so we parked outside. Walking through our Oriental-red front door, I hugged little Luke and Sofia, and headed straight to the master bedroom in the back of the house to nap.

Gifts littered our living-room floor. A new laptop, an iPod Touch, an Xbox with four controllers and six games. Boxes of books, DVDs, assorted toys for the kids. These came from coworkers and friends, some of whom I hadn't spoken with in years. Each person had placed considerable thought into their gift. Every gift was a lovely, heart-warming surprise. Charlotte, one of my friends at Microsoft, sent me a carefully curated collection of books and magazines affixed with Post-its illustrating the smiling likeness of Glinda the Good Witch (from *The Wizard of Oz*), upon which Charlotte—er...I mean "Glinda"— had handwritten the reason behind the selection.[17]

I organized all the presents as best I could into large, clear plastic crates, but the living room still resembled a garage sale.

Angela: Our friends and family showed incredible support, all of which was beautiful and hugely appreciated. Ultimately, though, I had to limit one-to-one communication—and offers of help—to just a small inner circle to keep from phone and email overload. And the blog Kevin created for Walt on lotsahelpinghands.com turned out to be a godsend as it provided me with a way to communicate with everyone without exhausting myself.

By nature, Walt is acutely private and self-reliant. By contrast, I grew up dependent on others, particularly given my stroke. Plus, in our large, extended Chinese-American family, each of us was an open book. Walt wasn't. I distinctly recall when Walt, on our first day at Overlake, asked to keep his leukemia private. I objected, explaining this was going to be a really long and arduous journey and that he had to consider the needs of me and the kids. We wouldn't survive without the help of friends (and family). Moreover, people wanted to help.

---

17   Another friend from Microsoft corralled a bunch of our colleagues into her kitchen to bake banana bread, which she auctioned off. $1,200!

While hooking up a bag of chemo, one of the nurses at Overlake couldn't help but overhear our discussion and artfully joined in my defense. 'Community is a must. You want people to know,' she said.

Walt may be stubborn, but he's logical—and certainly not intransigent. He recognized the wisdom and agreed we needed to be open.

One of the most valuable gifts I received came from someone I had met two weeks after my diagnosis. A friend's cousin, Ben, had been diagnosed with leukemia a few months before I was and, after several months of chemo, was slated to undergo a transplant. It was like he was a few steps ahead of me at the carnival.[18]

"Your world must feel completely upside down," Ben sympathized over the phone. "Know that it gets better." He asked me if I had a "dragon clip" for my Hickman line. "It's a tiny metal clothespin that hangs from a nylon necklace. You use it to clip and hold high the otherwise dangling ends of the Hickman line so that they don't get caught in the waistband of your pants. I don't know why they just don't hand them out. I'll send you one."

"Awesome, thanks! I appreciate that."

The dragon clip arrived three days later in a white business envelope. Once I started wearing it, I couldn't

---

18   https://en.wikipedia.org/wiki/Candy_Land

imagine being without. *Ben was right—they should hand these out...*

Almost the moment I got home, several friends and coworkers came to visit me, including Roger, my manager at Microsoft, whose wife I had told I had lymphoma the night I was racing with Angela and Kevin to Overlake before induction chemo. I was touched that Roger would take time off to drive all the way to my house. He lived pretty far away, and work kept him plenty busy.

It was a cold but unusually sunny afternoon when Roger, behind the wheel of the largest noncommercial truck I'd ever seen, pulled into my driveway. I don't recall the name, but it made the Chevy Suburban look like a Prius by comparison.

"This neighborhood is fantastic!" Roger gushed as he exited the driver's side door.

"Is that a hybrid?" I joked.

We entered the house, walked up the half-flight of stairs to the living room, and sat down on the same aqua-blue microfiber couch I'd lain upon, feeling flu-ish, the night before the ill-fated flight to San Jose.

"You look great!" Roger commented as we looked out onto the cul-de-sac through the floor-to-ceiling windows lining the front of the house. It had only been a week and the Hyper-CVAD hadn't yet changed my physical appearance. Looking at me, you'd never know I had cancer.

"Thanks."

We didn't have much to talk about other than work, which was fine, given that we were both workaholics. What else would we discuss?

"You're missed," he shared. "*Everyone* is asking about you. They keep coming by my office. Your absence has left a big hole."

"Wow, that's nice to hear." It was.

"Anything new going on?" I asked casually.

"You know. Chugging along. Nothing in particular other than your situation. I'm so sorry."

"Nothing to worry about. I don't feel any different."

In fact, I felt completely fine.

"Is there anything I can help with? Anything I can do?"

"I'm going to need to take time off."

"Of course."

Dr. Austin had warned me that I had to quarantine myself; that there would be no going into the office. I had to avoid contact with anyone or anything that could bring exposure to bacteria—or, God forbid, a virus. My white blood cell count was diving to zero, and I'd soon be defenseless against even the slightest infection, as is anyone undergoing systemic chemotherapy.

The following morning, I emailed my friend Seth (the

radiology oncologist) to ask if he had information about acute lymphoblastic leukemia. He ended up sending me two articles from the blandly named UpToDate.com, a reference database I heartily recommend if you want to get smart on any disease, although what follows may perhaps dissuade you.

UpToDate.com is a sophisticated medical resource full of detailed clinical data on a wide variety of illnesses in the form of briefs that read like CliffsNotes for medical texts. Seth sent me one written for patients and their families—a docile overview—and one intended for physicians—a wrenching enumeration of clinical trials and the associated survival rates.

I breezed through the brief written for patients. I choked, though, on the piece written for physicians, which contained not a single positive note, unless I missed one hiding somewhere in a dark corner hugging its knees. It was terrifying.

Here's a citation (bold font added):

*The survival rate [for ALL] at three years for patients less than 30 years old was 66 percent and for those **30 to 59 years old 36 percent.***

I was thirty-eight

Thirty-six percent?! That's it?

Another citation (bold and italicized font added):

> ***The majority of adults*** *with ALL who do attain an initial complete remission **will ultimately relapse.** Retreatment of such patients is **generally unsuccessful,** even with the use of hematopoietic cell transplantation (HCT), **and most will die of their disease.***

Holy shit! I'm going to die! This can't be right...

From blissful ignorance to the realization I'd been given a death sentence.

I couldn't sleep after seeing those numbers, at least not until dawn. Did I regret reading the brief? No. It probably wasn't the smartest thing to do in the middle of the night alone in a dark house. But better to know than not know.

In the months that followed, every doctor I came in contact with dodged any questions about odds. Instead, they defaulted to: "Everyone is different. In the end, you're either one hundred percent alive or one hundred percent dead." Everyone has different odds of survival and, maddeningly, none of us know what our own are. Plus, why worry about them if they're out of our control?

(Yeah, right. Try not worrying when staring down the barrel of a loaded leukemia rifle aimed directly at you. God bless you if you can.)

LADY LUCK

As poor as they can be to begin with, the odds of surviving leukemia hinge on at least three factors [19] along with things like age and general health:

- The patient has no blasts in the cerebrospinal fluid. Blasts are found only in the blood.

- The blasts don't carry a mutation called the "Philadelphia chromosome."

- The patient achieves full remission, meaning no detectable blasts remain within thirty days after the initial round of chemo.

Fortunately, there weren't any blasts in my cerebral spinal fluid so I could cross off #1. I worried, however, about #2—that the blasts in my blood might carry the Philadelphia chromosome, not unlikely given that one in four ALL patients proves positive for the mutation.[20] Two weeks had passed since diagnosis, and I still didn't know whether I was positive for the mutation. Thus four cards still lay face down on the blackjack table, any one of which could have shown positive for the Philadelphia chromosome. The dealer took his sweet, sweet time turning them over.

The wait was p-a-i-n-f-u-l.

"Are the results ready?" I'd ask Dr. Austin.

"Not yet."

---

19   At least this was the case at that time

20   http://www.haematologica.org/content/95/1/8

"Have the results come in?"

"Not yet."

"Results?"

"A few more days."

I couldn't get the question out of my mind.

One day, I was leaning back in a synthetic gray recliner getting chemo at Dr. Austin's clinic when Dr. Austin herself suddenly appeared. I wasn't scheduled to see her, but we ended up chatting anyway. Angela joined in. Nothing important. Just small talk. After a while, when Dr. Austin got up to leave, she turned around and, as if sharing an afterthought, said breezily, "Oh, good news—you are negative for the Philadelphia chromosome."

I can't believe she was so casual about that!

No Philadelphia chromosome, no blasts in my spinal fluid—check two of the three requisites for best odds of survival. Now there remained but one box: remission within thirty days of induction chemo.

Who knows, I might even end up like that guy Angela spoke to... Close to me in age, he had shared that he was eight years out from diagnosis. Married with two small children, he had beaten leukemia with chemo alone. No bone marrow transplant. No relapse. Just cured.

I wanted the same.

Had the first round of chemo put me in remission? Would I be able to check off three of the three indicators for best prognosis? Would I even need a transplant?

I walked by the young woman at the reception desk in Dr. Austin's clinic without stopping. She knew who I was, so there was no need to check in. As was the routine, I sat in one of the four identical chairs lining the hallway outside of the closet-sized blood lab, where on each visit a phlebotomist would extract vials of the viscous, violet fluid from my arm. Soon, Lisa, one of Dr. Austin's nurses, walked over with a warm greeting and led me to one of the several examination rooms in the back.

"Today's the big day!" she exclaimed.

"Yep."

My first biopsy.

"I'm going to take a sample of bone marrow from your hip," Dr. Austin explained after she joined us. "And don't worry, I'll give you some medicine so you'll feel sleepy. You won't feel a thing." I'm not ashamed to say I liked the high from the Versed, a nice break from all the stress, but I didn't get a chance to enjoy it for long. About one minute after the sedation began dripping into my arm I fell fast asleep.

On awakening, I felt but the slightest twinge of pain in my hip at the spot where Dr. Austin had extracted marrow.

Well, that was easy.

"How long until we get the results?" I asked Dr. Austin.

"Should take about three days. I'll give you a call once they're back."

Three days...I can handle that.

And so they passed.

Sitting in the living room at home, I heard the phone ring and stepped into the kitchen to pick it up.

"Hello..."

"Hi, Walt..."

Dr. Austin was on the line. Her voice was unusually soft, almost whispery.

"I'm afraid I have some bad news," she said gently. "The results from the biopsy came back. Your blast count is still at 49 percent. We're only halfway to where we need to be." The cordless phone still pressed against my ear, I hurried out of the kitchen down the photo-lined hallway to the master bathroom, where my family couldn't see me. I closed the door and leaned my head against a wall, crushed by the news.

"That's not good," I said, my voice on the verge of shaking.

"No, it's not. I'm so sorry."

"What do we do now?"

"I spoke to a number of people at the SCCA[21]

---

21   The Seattle Cancer Care Alliance, where Dr. Austin had performed a fellowship

and here's what I've decided. We need to switch chemo regimens. I've had you on Hyper-CVAD, and obviously that's not working. So I'm going to move you to Linker, an alternative that includes steroids."

Pause.

"And I need you to start tomorrow."

Angela: Up until this point, I had yet to see Walt deflated. Kevin, in fact, had coined a tagline for Team Walt: "If I were leukemia, I'd be scared." Kevin even made T-shirts, refrigerator magnets, and mugs featuring the tagline.[22] The bravado—and Kevin's amazing friendship and support—made us all feel better.

The phone call, though, was more than chilling. Walt looked pale.

"Worrying about it isn't going to change anything," said Jill, one of my favorite nurses, standing next to me the next day as I lay in bed, back in the cancer ward at Overlake. "You'll get through this." I knew she was trying to comfort me, but I was well aware of the clinical data I had read in the UpToDate.com article about the poor prognosis for refractory leukemia. Crestfallen, I knew things were likely not going to turn out well.

As I had with the week of Hyper-CVAD, I sailed through the week of Linker. Zero side effects save the fact my taste buds fell apart. All food tasted like burnt car tire. I tried to

---

22   http://www.zazzle.com/kasche

eat to keep my strength up, but between the foul taste of the food and a lack of appetite, I didn't eat much, though I tolerated a few chocolate shakes from the Overlake cafeteria.

Thinking comfort food might pique my interest, I ordered pizza and wings from Pizza Hut to be delivered to my room. What a disappointment. The food tasted like it had been marinated in machine oil, and I ended up tossing everything into the wastebasket.

A few weeks later, when I was back at home, the phone rang. It was Dr. Austin calling to share the results of the second biopsy. I'd find out if the new chemo protocol had worked or if, like the Hyper-CVAD, it had failed.

I took a deep breath and braced myself.

"Walt, your biopsy results came back."

Pause.

"Your blast count is now 19 percent. The Linker protocol is working..."

My heart leapt.

"That's fantastic!"

"I'm really, really happy for you," said Dr. Austin.

"Thank you! I'm beside myself!"

"So...we need to get you back in here for the next round. If we start two weeks from now, I should be able to get you home in time for Christmas. We also need to expedite your bone marrow transplant, which at this point is inevitable. It's clear that chemo alone won't keep your leukemia at bay. Our first task is to get you into full remission so you qualify for a transplant. That means getting your blast count to under 5 percent.[23] The SCCA won't admit you into the transplant program otherwise."

Hanging up the phone, I couldn't help but break up a bit as I shared the good news with Angela and her parents.

Angela: We were all standing at the kitchen island. I had never seen him get choked up like that—the relief was too great.

Now while the news was certainly encouraging, for the most part Walt and I were disconsolate about it all. Extremely so.

A couple of days after the buoyant phone call from Dr. Austin, the two of us lay in bed reading, our large black plasma TV on the wall staring at us, perhaps hoping we'd turn it on and stay up late. Walt put down his book, which he seemed to be barely following, and turned to me.

"We have life insurance," he said.

"I know," I replied without really paying attention.

---

23   Meaning blasts comprise less than 5 percent of my white blood cell count.

"I think I need to make videos for the kids just in case."

"Can we not talk about this right now?"

"This is like a fucking nightmare we can't wake up from," he said.

I finally put down my book as well.

Our lives had indeed become a nightmare, one that was hard to believe was real sometimes. Only, it was. Horribly so, and there was no making it go away. This surreal, haunting awfulness was our new normal. How did this happen? This was never part of the plan!

"I think the same thing every day. I wish we could make it stop," I said.

"I can't believe this is our life."

"I have some good news, though."

"Yeah?"

"Susan introduced me to her cousin. He was diagnosed with leukemia when he was twenty-eight. I spoke to him today. He's now thirty-six and married with two kids."

"Maybe we'll get lucky, too."

I looked at him. "You're not leaving me," I said. And I meant it. Plus, saying it out loud made it feel more possible. I turned off the lights, grabbed the remote, and turned on HGTV, our favorite channel for vegging, then slid next to Walt and rested my head on his shoulder. Together we watched in silence. And indeed we did stay up late.

At home with Sofia between chemo sessions (December 2008)

AMPUTATE?—DECEMBER 2008

A few weeks later, I found myself back in Dr. Hills' vascular surgery clinic.

"The graft is closing again," stated Dr. Chao, standing in for Dr. Hills, who was traveling. Two years had passed since the last time the graft in my left leg had failed. "I can go in to try to prevent collapse," he continued, "but your immune system is depleted from the chemo. There's an extremely high risk you could suffer infection from surgery, and that could easily prove fatal. I don't think we can afford the risk."

"But if we do nothing, I'll lose my foot, won't I?"

"Yes, you will," he replied, his words stark and unapologetic.

"The only way to avoid infection would be to give your immune system a chance to replenish. That would mean halting the chemo for at least a month."

I'm supposed to start the next round of Linker in less than two weeks. My blasts are still at 19 percent. There's no way we can put that off.

"I *have* to have the surgery on the graft. It's not a question," I told Dr. Chao. "I'm not going to lose my foot."

The next afternoon, I got a call from Dr. Chao.

"I talked with Dr. Austin. We agreed to have the surgery ten days from now. She thinks that should give your immune system enough time to replenish so that the risk of infection will be tolerable. You'll start chemo right after."

Good. I recognized it was a temporary fix—that the graft wouldn't last. But I wasn't about to have my leg amputated below the knee.

Angela: Well...the odd twist here is this: Dr. Chao and I went to college together. When he walked into the exam room, he said to me, "What are you doing here?" It was an odd and slightly awkward small-world moment. This was a guy I had spent time with around the keg at my boyfriend's residential college. That said, I knew he was smart.

Walt "interviewed" Dr. Chao (Henry) over the phone prior to surgery. Walt had huge confidence in Dr. Hills, but he wasn't familiar at all with Henry. And Henry didn't exactly exude self-assurance despite his extreme competence.

"I'm not doing this unless you tell me you've got it, Dr. Chao. I need you to quarterback this like a champ," Walt said with an uncharacteristic sports metaphor. "Can I count on that?"

Apparently, given that Walt went ahead with the procedure, Henry must have given the right answer.

As Angela had predicted, Dr. Chao came through, completing the graft repair without incident. No infection, no amputation. Blood was flowing to my left calf and foot again, and I had dodged yet another bullet.

The next day, Kevin came by to visit. And, of course, he brought his video camera. It wasn't the most exciting footage.[24] Basically it was me sitting in a chair while Luke recited the names of Bionicles and Sofia ran up to everyone screaming "peek-a-boo" as she hid her face behind the lid of her sippy cup. Luke and Sofia did, however, do a little hip-hop. That was sort of a highlight (http://bit.ly/2dAxCzc).

A couple of months later, the graft still holding strong, I went back to Dr. Hills' office for a regular checkup, where incredibly the ultrasound showed that the graft had miraculously *stopped* closing! Scar tissue was no longer amassing within the graft, no longer threatening to clog the causeway.

Unbelievable.

"I think the chemo you were on thwarted the growth of scar tissue," Dr. Hills told me later. "At least that's my theory. In fact, I think there's a case study here."

Given that chemo kills all rapidly dividing cells indiscriminately, why wouldn't chemo destroy the rapidly dividing cells of scar tissue accumulating in my graft and threatening to clog it yet again? Sure, I'm a sample set of one. Not really a cohort study. But I'll take it.

What an awesome turn of events. Chemo had saved my foot.

---

24   Add URL

At some point in December after Dr. Chao had performed his magic on the graft, I returned to work even though risk of fatal infection remained. Chemo had once again wiped out my immune system, and I was fearful of catching a flu virus from any colleague who might be sick (after all, it was flu season) or touching bacteria on door handles and conference-room tables that might be harmless for most people—but not for me. Still, I loved my job and had to get out of the house. So I rigged a system in my office that, at least in my mind, minimized risk. I created a fortress of isolation, turning my office into a self-contained germ shelter. I was to be a "boy in the bubble" with everything I needed safe within its confines. Microwave, mini-refrigerator, printer, high-end conference phone—everything. I carefully placed bottles of hand sanitizer in strategic locations around the room and stacked canisters of Clorox sanitizing wipes atop my desk. And I kept the door closed. The moment anyone came into my office, I would ask them to sanitize their hands, so regularly that it got to where I didn't have to ask—people just walked directly to one of the gel dispensers upon entering.

Not that the round conference table in my office really needed it, but I cleaned the surface multiple times a day. I never touched any of the door handles in the building with my bare hands but instead grabbed them with my hand covered by a shirtsleeve. And my pants pockets were *never* without a travel-size bottle of sanitizer, which I rubbed into my palms and fingers every ten minutes. Obsessively.

No in-person meetings, no travel—those were my self-imposed rules. I was to stay within the safe walls of the fortress, which I was fully prepared to do. Or at least that was the plan. But when day one arrived—my first day back—I noticed a team meeting on my Outlook calendar slated for 10 a.m.

That's why you have the fancy speakerphone, Walt. Dial in—you'll be fine.

I broke my own rule, of course. I didn't even make it past one meeting, much less one day. I wanted to be in the same room as everyone else. I didn't want to dial in, regardless of how fancy the speakerphone in my fortress was. And the desire simply outweighed the risk.

People around the long table inside the brightly lit conference room began clapping the moment I entered. "That's one sexy-looking bald man!" the team's general manager called out.

I walked to the back of the room, where one open seat remained, a broad smile across my face. I couldn't have been happier. No more isolation, no more loneliness, no more lack of distraction, no more endless perseveration over worst-case scenarios.

Angela: Walt was stubborn about going back to work. But I knew that despite the risk, it was the healthiest thing he could do. He had always been a workaholic, and at times his drive outweighed all reason. I defended his choice to friends and family.

Did it prove to be the wrong decision in the end? Hard to say. Walt could've hidden in a sealed closet at home and things still might have turned out the same.

DEVASTATION

The next day at work I received an email from Seth, the radiation oncologist who had sent me the articles from UpToDate.com. He suggested that I check out the story of a fellow Stanford grad who had leukemia, someone named Richard. In retrospect, I think I misinterpreted Seth's message.

Someone to connect with? Cool. Maybe he has advice.

Seth's intentions were truly good; I just didn't realize what I was getting into.

The first thing I did was search for Richard's name on the web, which I found on the first try. It turned out that not only did Richard and I both attend Stanford, but we were also both in our thirties when diagnosed. We both lived on Mercer Island[25] (or rather Richard's parents did, but he lived with his parents during treatment). And Richard went through his transplant via the SCCA, something I, too, was slated to do (assuming I could get my blast count low enough).

Richard's blog was a dramatic, time-sequenced narrative

---

25   Mercer Island is a community of approximately twenty thousand people in the middle of Lake Washington adjacent to Seattle.

laden with a mix of medical explanation and emotion. As is the case with most cancer blogs, the entries appeared in reverse chronological order, newer entries before older ones. So the first thing I read on Richard's cancer blog was the story's ending. Which was chilling. While some cancer stories I read at the time ended well, others, like Richard's, did not. The most recent entry on the blog provided the place, date, and time of Richard's memorial service.

A dozen colorful photos brought life to the home page of Richard's blog. One showed an athletic and vibrant young man in his prime surrounded by friends, another was a wedding portrait of a dashing prince standing beside a spouse prettier than Audrey Hepburn in her heyday. In various other photos, Richard had lost his hair and eyebrows. Whereas in the non-cancer pictures his face was rosy, in others it was ashen. But he smiled regardless. A man others described as bright and ebullient, he was clearly a source of light and energy for those around him.

Even though I knew how this was going to end, I, of course, felt wholly compelled to read the story from the start, so I clicked on the very first entry, one dated one year earlier almost to the day. It told how Richard was diagnosed with leukemia during a trip to Taipei, Taiwan. Shocked, he flew home to Seattle to start treatment immediately at the University of Washington Medical Center. Richard was only thirty years old. He'd never been in a hospital bed.

I read. And read. As fast as I could for two hours. Absorbed. I couldn't pull myself away.

Richard achieved remission after his first round of chemo. Good for his prognosis. He and his family were ecstatic. But two months later, he relapsed, something he shared in an entry titled 'Setback,' which it was indeed. Relapses, particularly so soon after initial remission, do not portend well.

Chemo wasn't enough. Richard needed a bone marrow transplant as soon as possible to survive, and for that he needed a bone marrow (stem cell) donor with genetic markers matching his own. The most likely candidate for a genetic match? A sibling (but even then it's a roll of the dice—only a percentage of siblings are matches). Unfortunately, that wasn't an option for Richard—he had no siblings. The next best option? Find a match in one of the world's bone marrow registries, databases with privately guarded information regarding select genetic markers voluntarily submitted by millions of potential donors (and, therefore, lifesavers).[26] Tragically, none of the millions of donors in the world's registries contained a match for Richard—not a single one— which is not surprising given that the majority of registered donors, at least in the US, are of white, European descent.[27] Richard was Indian.

Richard's friends immediately rose to the occasion,

---

26   It only takes a mere cheek swab sent by mail to get into the database, something that can be transacted in the US online through the National Marrow Donor Program at bethematch.org. Outside of the US, you can find and contact a local registry through the listing at BMDW.org.

27   http://mixedmarrow.org/statistics-and-information.

launching an online bone marrow drive calling for people in the Indian community to register as donors. In doing so, they generated thirty-five thousand registrants in a week. And incredibly—incredibly—one of them turned out to be a perfect match!

"MISSION ACCOMPLISHED!" read the title of Richard's next entry.[28]

Joy poured from the page, spirits soared!

A month later, Richard posted a photo of himself receiving the donor's stem cells via a simple IV drip—an image that looked as if he were simply receiving a pint of blood. No fanfare. Yet that day was Richard's "new birthday," as they say in the transplant world.

I stared at the image for several minutes. It was so peaceful.

Richard's journal went quiet for a while until he posted a new entry that fast-forwarded to his recovery at home. In it, Richard spoke briefly of his carefree life post-transplant: walks with his wife, the comfort of his parents' house, and visits with his care team at the SCCA, who raved about how well he was doing. Richard quoted them saying, "You're doing better than 99 percent of our patients!" So well, he said, that the team reduced his clinical visits from two per week to one. As he had done often in life, Richard had triumphed—things were going his way.

---

28   Richard's name and the details of his blog have been changed for privacy. Trust me, though, this is what the narrative read like.

That is, until two weeks later. Richard's father posted an entry that shattered the euphoria.

"We learned today that Richard has again relapsed."

Richard must have been *crushed*.

"The doctors asked me if I wanted to just walk away," Richard wrote a few days later. "They wanted to know if I was up for running the gauntlet again—making another go at a stem cell transplant. I asked them, 'Who do you think you're talking to? *Of course* I'm in!'"

First step is to get back to remission. Right now my blast count is 22 percent. To qualify for a second transplant, it needs to drop to under 5 percent."

The plan was for Richard, upon re-achieving remission, to receive another injection of the stem cells he'd received from his donor, the remainder of which had been frozen. But to get Richard's blast count under 5 percent, doctors had to use a highly potent experimental chemo, the prospect of which made both Richard and his family anxious.

Mercifully, not only did Richard survive the powerful chemical onslaught, he also achieved the desired result—remission! Richard's next entry read: "A MIRACLE! The biopsy yesterday showed my blast level at 3.1 percent! No one can understand how it could have happened. The doctors are mystified. It's indeed a miracle! I am blessed! We will now prepare for the stem cell boost."

Once again celebration burst forth on the page. Everyone

was ecstatic.

And then there was silence.

An awful silence.

For a week.

No updates at all. At least not until the thunder cracked.

"It looks like we celebrated too soon," wrote Richard, his tone clearly crestfallen. "The doctors checked again, and my blast count is 34 percent, *not* 3.1 percent. The 3.1 percent count resulted from the doctors testing marrow in just *one* of my hip bones. The *other* hip bone shows 34 percent while the original has since jumped back up to 12 percent."

He must have felt incredibly disconsolate and afraid. What a setup, what a ghastly fall.

Days later, Richard was sent to the ICU, his body ravaged by staphylococcus, a bacterial infection that lives on everyone's skin but is kept at bay by our immune systems. Except that Richard had no immune system. From then on, Richard posted no more entries. He couldn't: he was unconscious. The remaining few came from his father. Including this one:

"The doctors say Richard suffered a stroke today. We pray for him to come back to us."

That's it. He's going to die—and he isn't even aware of what's happening.

Two days later, Richard's father posted once more:

As most of you know by now, Richard left us this morning a little before 5 a.m. for a higher place. He left after a valiant struggle with leukemia and the subsequent accumulation of issues from multiple chemotherapies.

We felt the love of the many doctors and nurses who looked after him and exerted great effort to nurture him to health, and we thank you all for that.

Yes, I had known where the story was headed, yet still I sat frozen in horror when I got there again. Not so much from Richard's death, which was tragic, but from the torturous ups and downs he endured, a nine-month psychological whipsawing between hope and terror. And a death he wasn't even aware of—he just fell away.

Richard had lived in the same city that I did. He, too, had been entrepreneurial, active, and ambitious. He and I went to the same university. He went through a transplant at the University of Washington via the SCCA, the same route I was destined to take.

Will this be my story?

My back was tense and my eyes red when I opened the front door at home that night.

"Are you ok?" Angela asked, still wearing the black blouse and skirt she had worn to work. "What happened? You look terrible!" I told her the story and later sent her the URL.

Poor Seth. A day later he got a searing call from my wife. The guy didn't deserve it. He was sincerely trying to help, but Angela didn't take it that way.

"Why would you send something like that to my husband?!"

Listen, I was glad he did. Truly. As terrible and tragic and frightening as Richard's story was, I now had no misconception as to what might lie ahead. Though it was something of a curse—I was aware of what could come crashing down, as well as when and how—it was also a blessing in that I was now armed against over-optimism. Sure, I might die—that was out of my control—but I wasn't going to let any high points along the way delude me into euphoria. I wasn't going to be emotionally whipsawed. I wasn't going to over-celebrate. I was going to keep to the middle.

My time back at work proceeded apace with no major issues until one evening when a good friend tapped on my office window and mouthed the words, "You look sick! Go home!"

Ari was right. I really did feel fatigued. "OK," I mouthed back. So I packed up, made my way to the parking lot, and started down the 520 freeway toward home.

I didn't get very far.

Hiccup...! Hiccup...!

I'd been suffering from chronic hiccups ever since the last round of Linker. On for a week, off for a couple of days. On for a week, off for a couple of days. Now they were back. In fact, they'd been back all day. Conversations at work had gone like this:

"Well, I...*hic*...think perhaps we should...*hic*...do it this way...*hic!*"

Exhausting. And the hiccups had become worse as the day went on. I was definitely ready to go home and glad Ari had said something. But the further I drove, the more frequent and intense the diaphragmatic spasms grew, until ultimately I became so dizzy that I almost fainted. Which is why I pulled off an exit and parked.

"Angela, I need you to come get me," I said over the phone, my teeth clenched.

"Where are you?"

I gave her my location, then lowered my head onto the steering wheel to rest. Fifteen minutes later, Angela pulled up behind me. After one look, she said, "We're going to the emergency room," which thankfully was located only a few blocks away. We didn't, though, think to contact Dr. Austin en route so that she could give staff at the Overlake Emergency Room a heads-up about my condition. Instead, we went in anonymously.

Although there was no one else waiting in the ER lobby, the man at the admitting desk took his time before even looking up at us. When he did finally speak, he asked halfinterestedly, "What's the matter?"

"I have severe hiccups," I explained.

The man stared at me with incomprehension.

"What?"

"Hiccups. And I'm dizzy. I feel like I'm going to pass out."

"Hm...okay," he mumbled skeptically. He took my information and sent us away to the waiting area, where I grew increasingly miserable. My entire body shook with each hiccup, which were now coming just seconds apart. Finally, after what seemed like a birthday later, a nurse called my name and led us to the back. There she took her time walking through the standard litany of questions required for admission, had me stand on a scale, and eventually just sat there typing silently at her keyboard.

The wait was torturous.

I finally spoke up, embarrassed at my own vulnerability. "I can usually withstand a lot"—I could—"but these hiccups are really debilitating and painful."

No response.

She probably thinks I'm ridiculous. Who comes to the emergency room for hiccups?

I wasn't too far off in my assessment. After I finally landed in an exam room, I overheard two emergency-room staff whispering to each other outside my doorway.

"I guess that hiccups are now a reason to come to the

emergency ward!" said the male assistant, causing the female assistant to giggle in response.

The male turned out to be my nurse. Well-built, with thick orange hair swept back atop his head, he skated into my room and brashly pronounced with a subtle smirk on his face, "You should try drinking Orange Crush while standing on your head! That'll cure your hiccups!"

I should try punching you in the face.

Orange Crush took my blood pressure and temperature, the latter showing 101 degrees.

"You've got a fever," he said. "That's all. You should go home and get some rest."

Angela: I ended up explaining to the attending physician that Walt was neutropenic, which made her concerned.[29] Suddenly, these weren't just the hiccups and a fever. This was an immunosuppressed cancer patient with a temperature.

"I suggest that we admit Walter to the cancer ward," the doctor said to me. Walt, of course, resisted.

"I don't need to be admitted." He didn't want to be wrested from his life yet again. So I declined the doctor's recommendation.

---

29   A patient is considered neutropenic when they have an extremely low white blood cell count, as was the case with Walt due to the chemo he was undergoing. People who are neutropenic are highly susceptible to infection and dangerously underequipped to fight it.

"I don't think that's a wise choice," the doctor warned, now irritated. "In fact, if you take him home, don't bring him back when things get worse."

I should've stood my ground. Walt should've been admitted.

When I woke up in our bedroom at midnight, I felt completely disoriented. Tapping Angela on the shoulder, I asked her to take my temperature, something I never did (it was always the reverse).

"Are you feeling hot?" she asked.

"Yes."

She walked into the bathroom and returned with our store-bought digital thermometer. After wiping down the business end with a cotton ball dipped in rubbing alcohol, Angela slipped it under my tongue. At the beep, she pulled it out and looked down.

105 degrees.

High for anyone. Deadly for someone with a shattered immune system.

I have three memories from that night: 1) waking up to ask Angela to take my temperature, 2) hearing Angela say "105 degrees," and 3) a hazy image of three paramedics in blue uniforms leaning over me as they carried me out of my house on a stretcher.

"You'll be alright. We have you," said one of the

paramedics as he helped ferry me down the hallway. Outside, an ambulance waited in my driveway, its red lights flashing.

I don't recall the ensuing two weeks. Blackout.

Angela: The paramedic was kind to Walt. Still, I could tell he was freaked out when he asked me whether Walt had a DNR (do not resuscitate) order as we rode in the back of the rig. My inner voice said, "Shut up and just get him to Overlake."

I think it was in that ambulance when I realized I needed to develop a thicker skin when it came to pushing back on Walt's stubbornness. That was a hard lesson to learn.

When we arrived at Overlake we went directly to the cancer ward, where Dr. Austin had called ahead. There we were met by a kind nurse with an Eastern European accent so thick I couldn't decipher what was coming out of her mouth. And she wasn't a "take charge" nurse—the kind I like. In fact, she was floundering, which made me anxious.

Someone sent us to get an x-ray in the basement despite the fact that Walt had gotten an x-ray done there just hours earlier when we met Orange Crush. I didn't care so much that we were duplicating efforts. I was concerned that, given his neutropenia, the more Walt travelled around the germy hospital, the greater were his chances of infection.

None of the orderlies were wearing gloves or in the mood to pay attention to my concerns, so I made it my right to go along to the basement with Walt. And I'm glad I did. Once there, the x-ray technician (also ungloved and unmasked) and the orderlies struggled to prop Walt upright so they could take an x-ray. Walt was barely conscious. Despite the team's efforts, he kept flopping over. Everyone refused to acknowledge my suggestion to save Walt the trial and simply track down the x-ray that already existed. They had their orders (to take an x-ray) and were going to do as they were told.

"You need to be more careful!" I shouted.

The technician looked at me in annoyance and asked snidely, "Who are you?"

"I'm the wife," I replied.

He didn't expect that. I could see the "Oh, crap" look on his face when I told him who I was. His response was "Sorry, I thought you were the nurse," which was a little frightening. That's how you react to nurses? I thought. Still, he switched to a more careful approach.

Because I didn't trust the care Walt was getting, I spent the night in his room rather than going home to be with the kids. The nurses counseled me to go home—"to get some rest."

Hell, no. I wasn't leaving Walt alone in this monkey house.

I waited until Dr. Austin came by for rounds in the morning. After I told her what had happened, she arranged for only the best nurses—the ones we knew and trusted—to care for Walt.

Finally, I felt comfortable leaving Walt and went home to crash.

Whirr-whirr...Whirr-whirr...Whirr-whirr...

Unaware that nearly half a month had gone by, I opened my eyes to find a large white plastic leech sucking on my calf—a vacuum-assisted closure device the hospital had placed there to keep moisture out of the deep gash located there.[30]

Whirr-whirr...

Turns out I had contracted a severe E. coli infection, resulting in the formation of abscesses (pockets of pus) in five places: my lower back, the left and right side of my waist, my left leg (the gash that the leech was sucking on), and, well, my anus. Ergo the 105-degree temperature, delirium, and ambulance trip back to Overlake.

It was the abscess in my rectum that had stumped the doctors. They had discovered and removed all the other abscesses, yet the infection continued to rage. At least

---

30   VAC therapy is used to keep wounds that can't be stitched closed clean and dry so they can heal.

until a nurse—Nicky, one of my favorites—happened to discover the holdout in the seat of my pants.

Walter's Bedside Blog

It's been a tough week: Walt's back in the hospital

Posted by Angela Lean on Sunday 01/18/2009

For folks who may not already know, Walt unfortunately landed back in the hospital with an infection this week, and with chemo already scheduled to begin next Monday, it looks like he's going to be in for a 10- to 14-day stretch.

After two-plus months of relatively manageable chemo and a modicum of normalcy, this experience has given both of us a huge reality dose/reminder of how hard this can be and, unfortunately, things to come. Apparently, infections of this sort are incredibly common for folk with ALL and the doctor has been amazed that it's taken this long for him to get one.

On the brighter side, he's doing better now—with little to no fever and somewhat better stamina. The doctors have identified the source of the infection and are aggressively treating him with antibiotics.

Of course, there have been a few true Walt moments through all of this, including his Will Farrell imitation and "pageant walking" for me and the nurses during his first official walk around the oncology ward. At the same time, it's incredibly disappointing for us and the kids to have him back in the hospital for such a long period of time.

My goal is to be back at work on Monday and with the help and support of my extended "pit crew" (both here in Seattle and beyond), I've so far been able to juggle being at the hospital, taking care of the kids, and theoretically staying sane. I'm once again astounded by everyone's support and incredibly grateful. THANK YOU.

Unfortunately, Walt's cell phone is on the fritz (I'm working on getting that fixed ASAP) and we've been limiting visitors due to his energy level and weakened immune system. Best way to reach him for now would be via email or this blog. In fact, I know emails, well wishes, etc. make a huge difference lifting his spirits, so as much support (as possible) over the next couple of weeks would be great.

Folks should also feel free to check in with me as time progresses and he gets in better shape to have more visitors. We can use all the positive energy we can get.

Best, Angela

Years later, Dr. Austin shared with me that of all my time under her care, it was during the infection with E.

coli that she was most concerned for my life. And I slept through it. What I didn't sleep through, though, was the aftermath. Emptying my bowels with an open wound in the path, the excavated abscess in my rectum, generated a searing burn. And not to be too gross, but wiping only made matters worse (scrubbing raw tissue). Had I only needed an occasional bowel movement, I probably could have endured the pain by clenching a leather belt in my teeth. Unfortunately, I had severe diarrhea, which meant I was constantly on the toilet. The stinging was so severe that I ended up pounding my fist on the tile walls. A nurse offered me a sitz bath, meaning I sat naked in a shallow bowl of fizzy water, but that didn't help. So I switched from toilet paper to baby wipes. That provided a bit of relief.

The divots in my skin, particularly the massive gash in my leg that was so deep it exposed tendons, required regular, labor-intensive cleaning and re-bandaging. So elaborate was the work that after I went home the hospital had to send a specialist daily for the sole purpose of treating and dressing the laceration. Eventually, when the specialist stopped coming, the responsibility for wound care transferred to Angela and me.

A nurse in the wound care clinic at Swedish Hospital in downtown Seattle told me that the cut in my leg probably wouldn't heal because of the chemo I was on. She said that I would likely need to graft pigskin over it, else the hole would be left open to infection—a fact that later served as a point of contention as to whether or not to delay my transplant. No one wanted to proceed if I had a big hole in my leg.

Angela: I was the one consistent witness to Walt's wound care. Each time a new medical team came across the divot in his leg, they'd inevitably become alarmed. "How do you take care of that?" they would ask.

We were in a race to transplant, but the doctors and nurses were hesitant to proceed until the laceration healed. It was becoming a blocker.

Walter's Bedside Blog

Two surgeries and another round of chemo down, transplant in March

Posted by Angela Lean on Thursday 01/22/2009

I just returned from the hospital and am happy to report that Walt was dozing off to sleep after a post-operative meal of Fat Burger's best (c/o Kev Ascher—thanks Kev!). I can't tell you how great it was to see him sitting up, with good color in his face and joking around with all of us, docs and nurses included.

He ended up having two surgeries to drain the abscess in his leg this week. Thankfully, both went well and the blood culture from his leg no longer shows evidence of any E. coli bacteria. He also has not had a fever since yesterday. :-)

He finished this last round of chemo today, and we received word that we are now tracking to an early March transplant date (vs. April as had been previously expected). This assumes no other infections/complications, he stays in remission and they get the donor all lined up—but all in all it's good news and we're jumping on the opportunity.

We are making progress, but this last week is certainly one for the record books with regard to stress. Walt is continually poked, prodded, and tortured at all hours of the day and night. Both kids, the nanny, and the babysitter all got sick with various ailments. My mom and I were quite literally the last ones standing at home, and at one point I found myself openly weeping over the prospect of lost keys—not my shining moment.

It's still unclear how long Walt will remain at Overlake, but I am hopeful he will have more energy to be in better contact by the weekend. One of us will update you all if new news comes in.

Best, Angela

SARA'S STORY, FEBRUARY 2009

I read at least a handful of blogs about people with leukemia—some that unfolded in real time along with mine, others, like Richard's, that recorded recent history. Some blogs were inspiring, others horrific. Sara's story landed right in the middle.

Sara, a young mother of two, had lived a radiant life, ably organizing activities for her two sons, cooking feasts for friends and family, and advising CEOs on business strategy as a successful corporate consultant.

Sadly, Sara contracted ALL at age thirty-five.

She went through a transplant, but, like Richard, later relapsed. And when the doctors realized they couldn't halt the growth of blasts in her blood, she found her situation terminal.

Because of the deep bonds Sara had built with many friends in her life, she never had to worry about her family's welfare. Whenever she was waylaid by the debilitating side effects of treatment, friends showered her family with food, care, and love to keep their lives on the rails. So winsome was Sara that one time when she needed cross-country transportation but couldn't take a commercial flight because her dangerously suppressed immune system left her too vulnerable to infection, the chairman of one of the Fortune 500 companies she advised sent his corporate jet to ferry her home. A couple of months later, on hearing that her condition was worsening, the producers of *Lost*, the hit TV show that held a vast American audience entranced, phoned Sara in her hospital room. They called to address a small regret Sara had jokingly shared the day before—that she wasn't going to be around to find out how the series ended. Over the phone, the producers, who happened to be friends of friends of friends, read her the script for the final episode, a story they were keeping under lock and key.

Sara knew she didn't have much time to live, yet with resolute focus, she continued to tend to those she cherished. She even took steps to extend her caring hand beyond her impending death by drafting a guidebook for her husband on the intricacies of scheduling playdates for their boys, including names of favorite pals, contact numbers for parents, and common date times. She taped videos, compiled photos, and archived memories for her children that would otherwise inevitably fade and disappear.

Within a week of filming the videos, Sara suffocated to death as a result of a severe lung infection brought on by immunodeficiency. The blasts in her blood had crowded out the last of her healthy white blood cells, leaving her defenseless to attack.

GETTING TO TRANSPLANT

The chemo session that followed the abscess drama managed to get my blast count to just 0.2 percent, well under the 5 percent minimum required by the SCCA for transplant. So I was ready. The time had come, just four months out from diagnosis in Mountain View, to graduate from Dr. Austin's clinic and enroll at the SCCA for the big next step.

When it comes to treatment for leukemia, few places on the planet rival the Seattle Cancer Care Alliance. The SCCA combines medical personnel and researchers from three organizations: The Fred Hutchinson Cancer Research Center ('the Hutch'), Seattle Children's Hospital, and the University of Washington Medical Center. It was at the Hutch that a team of physicians led by Nobel Prize winner Dr. E. Donnall Thomas invented the bone marrow transplant, a treatment that has since saved thousands of lives.

The SCCA itself is not a hospital, but rather a holistic beehive of outpatient care housed in a modern, seven-story brick building in downtown Seattle. The SCCA overlooks the small but scenic Lake Union, popular with sailboat owners and bordered by nautical repair shops, floating houses, and restaurants. The facility is clean and well-appointed. Comfortable, bright, smartly designed furniture fills each floor, giving the interior a fresh, warm ambiance. A long arched desk welcomes patients at the entrance on the first floor. Alongside are the blood-draw unit, the business office, and an information kiosk. During flu season, the SCCA requires patients and visitors to first check in at a card table placed next to the reception desk.

There, using the honor system, they are to answer a short series of questions intended to identify whether or not they have a cold or the flu. The times when I did indeed have a cold, I was required to wear a mask and sit in waiting room areas cordoned off for the sick. The SCCA touts that it is in part its conscientiousness about preventing the spread of infection that has led to its success rates in "turning patients into survivors." To maintain a hyper-sanitary environment, SCCA staff clean every bathroom in the building several times a day. Seriously. They clean them *several* times a day.

On a dark night in late February, I attended an orientation meeting for transplant patients, bringing with me a light-blue plastic bowl equal in size to my head. Not Tupperware by brand but certainly equivalent in genre, the bowl served as a receptacle for the intermittent eruption of vomit caused by the hiccups that still persisted. Angela and I sat next to each other at a low, round table covered in white Formica in an otherwise featureless room. A bespectacled young physician to my right hovered over a stack of papers, and a female nurse stared me down without a hint of humor from the other side of the room.

What's she so angry about?

Before I go on, let me first say that when it comes to physicians, I don't care a thing about their demeanor (unless they're downright rude—and I have yet to meet one who is). They can be grim, funny, friendly, cold, awkward, whatever. Regardless of their disposition, I view them as one thing and one thing only—talented and trained professionals dedicated to helping others and, in my case, saving my life.

All the physicians at the SCCA, without exception, are good Samaritans, including the young man next to me at the table that night. Still, his manner of delivery merits a bit of light, respectful teasing, if only because it was unforgettable.

Without looking up from the papers in front of him, Dr. John Harrison began to speak quietly, but with determination. Almost immediately it became obvious that Dr. Harrison was dead set on walking through whatever script it was that he held in his hands *exactly* as it was written—no paraphrasing, no shortcuts. Word for word. And at an excruciatingly slow pace. To make matters worse, he took awkwardly long pauses every few sentences as if to give Angela and me a moment to digest what he was saying. All of which was, well, straightforward.

The gist of his message? If I didn't go through with the transplant, I was going to die for any number of reasons—a moot point, given that I already welcomed the prospect of transplant. I was already singing the transplant song, yet, like a skipping record, Dr. Harrison kept driving the point home. Relentlessly. Time and again he repeated the phrase: "If [xyz thing] happens or [abc thing] doesn't happen and you don't go through with a transplant, you will die," although there was occasional variation on the theme:

"Blah, blah, blah without a transplant, you will die."

Awkwardly long pause...

"Fa, fa, fa absent transplant will mean death."

Awkwardly long pause...

"Fi, fi, fi without a transplant will result in death."

Yet another awkwardly long pause...

I kid you not. These were the exact sentences coming out of his mouth with the exact cadence. Surreal. Perhaps he was legally required to enumerate word for word specific disclosures about the consequences of not proceeding with the transplant. Who knows?

As Dr. Harrison held forth, I intermittently—and of necessity—raised the blue plastic bowl to my face so I could capture the sour juices surfacing from my empty stomach due to the convulsions in my diaphragm.

Hiccup!

Urrp!

GUUURGGHH!

"If da, da, da without a transplant, you will die."

I stood up to go to the bathroom.

After I left, Angela turned to Dr. Harrison. "I think he understands the dangers," she explained gently. "And he's committed to the transplant. I think we can fast forward a little."

"There is a thirty-five percent mortality rate associated with the side effects of transplant," Dr. Harrison explained when I returned to the table. What he meant was that I had a 35 percent chance of dying from graft-versus-host disease (GVHD), a phenomenon that occurs when the donor's stem cells, newly introduced into the patient's system, mature into white blood cells that don't recognize their surroundings. The new white blood cells mistakenly attack cells of the liver, lungs, and heart, which leads to organ failure and death.

"You also have a thirty-five percent chance of dying from relapse."

When Dr. Harrison finished, I stared at the pie chart I had sketched on a yellow legal pad while he was talking: a circle with three triangular pieces marked 35 percent, 35 percent, and 30 percent, representing respectively the odds I faced for dying from GVHD, dying from relapse, and surviving for some undetermined period.

I stared at the smaller of the triangles, the one marked 30 percent. *Will I be one of the lucky ones who land in that pie piece?*

After the orientation and with our breath visible in the night air, Angela and I walked out into the cold parking garage, both of us dumbfounded. The last time I had felt such post-traumatic shock was after seeing *Pulp Fiction* for the first time on a big screen.

What just happened?

"Are you kidding me?" I blurted involuntarily.

What we had experienced was so over the top, it was farcical. I couldn't help but laugh. Angela looked at me with half a smile, as she, too, was incredulous. And, like me and fortunately for me, she has a healthy sense of humor, even in dark moments. You'd think we both would have been shaken to the core by Dr. Harrison's death litany, but we weren't. We were instead flabbergasted, almost giddy from how unreal the whole thing was.

To this day, the moment one of us mentions that meeting with Dr. Harrison, we both laugh. It's a go-to inside joke.

"If bloop, bleep, blop...you will die."

Awkwardly long pause.

"Roger called today," Angela told me one afternoon after I walked through the door from my daily visit to the SCCA for transplant prep. Earlier that day, President Obama had announced the Homeowner Affordability and Stability Plan, a $75 billion federal initiative that would enable people impacted by the economic meltdown, whose homes were worth less than 80 percent of the value of their mortgages, to refinance. Meanwhile, Fannie Mae reported a 2008 loss of a whopping $58.7 billion, greedy and teetering AIG received $30 billion in a government bailout, and the US unemployment rate hit 8.3 percent, a steep increase from 4.9 percent a year prior. Millions of Americans had lost their jobs—724,000 in February alone—as had millions more worldwide. In a move that would have seemed like science fiction a few decades earlier, the federal government was making preparations to take control of iconic automakers General Motors and Chrysler.

It was an apocalypse.

Citing deteriorating global economic conditions, Microsoft announced it would be cutting up to five thousand jobs, 5.5 percent (!) of its global workforce— about five thousand people. Microsoft had *never* held mass layoffs. The news struck me as an unreal, yet at the same time obvious. Of course they had to cut back like everyone else.

This made me nervous.

"So what did Roger say?"

"He just called to say we shouldn't worry, that your job isn't in jeopardy."

Wow, that was thoughtful of him.

Just like it was thoughtful of him to keep me at full salary as long as possible before I had to go on short-term disability and take a pay reduction.

GRACE UNDER FIRE

Should a transplant fail, one alternative to rescue therapy (another term for last-defense chemo) is to, well, walk away—

literally. Leave the hospital and pass in peace at home. Ben, the man who had kindly sent me the dragon clip for my Hickman line the week after I was diagnosed with leukemia, chose to do exactly that. He decided to end his journey as the warm-up to my transplant was getting started.

Ben didn't give up, mind you. He considered his situation and made the conscious choice to spend his final days not in a hospital bed but rather at home, in an environment of his choosing, with the family he cherished by his side.

This is the last entry he wrote in his blog:

It was great while it lasted![31]

Who likes sharing bad news? So maybe the good news...currently I am feeling well and it doesn't look like I need to worry a great deal about the frailties of old age. The latest bone marrow (transplant) did not turn out as we had hoped. In essence the blast cells (leukemia) are coming back too early for the transplanted stem cells to have a foothold or fighting chance. So I am now on the advanced course in life of what is important and what is not. The important things in life, as you know, are friends, family and the beauty of each moment. I sincerely thank all of you for the tremendous support we have received over the last year and a half from family and friends. I thank you in advance for the continued support of my family as they

---

31   Reprinted with permission.

encounter change and loss. My worries are likely to be over this spring and I won't need help or support. As a dear friend's mother commented to her hospice nurse, "Honey, don't worry about me, I'm going on the adventure of a lifetime." I'm going to get the real lesson on how everything is connected. I could have waited for the lesson, but these things are out of our control.

With life in general, I could have behaved better at moments (forgive me my trespasses) but feel I have had the best life possible and have no major regrets. If I project into the future, I can be saddened by my own absence at key junctions in the life of family and friends. Generally this thought process has proved unhelpful and sets a poor example for them, so I try not to go there; back to enjoying the NOW. I am incredibly pleased and proud of Lisa and Chris. They are great students that have made great life choices. They fortunately are not a source of worry. Lisa has a wonderful and unique group of friends and extended family. She may not feel it yet, but she too will do fine.

The future moments not realized has just made the past and present more precious. Love to all, Brian.

P.S. We have just moved back home. It is so enjoyable to be here.

I imagined what I would do were I to end up in the

same position as Brian—not an unrealistic proposition. I envisioned taking my family to Hawaii and spending our last days together playing in the sand, swimming with turtles, and napping on the grass underneath tall, bending palms.

Yes, that is what we'd do.

The following blog post came a month later from Brian's wife.

The Next Great Adventure

In true Brian-fashion, it seems most fitting to begin with the good news. In his own words, he's on to "the next great adventure." As many of you already know, our beloved [Brian] passed away on Monday, April 6 at 7 p.m. The day was sunny and warm, with Mt. Baker ever-present. It was undoubtedly the most glorious spring-like day we've had all year. He was surrounded by family and friends and left us peacefully and painlessly. That evening we toasted him with an Irish microbrew he would have approved of and shared many fond memories.

CHEMO HOLIDAY

Following the surreal orientation with Dr. Harrison, I was left with a two-week countdown to my transplant, a period during which I would receive no chemo. Because of this respite, my white blood cell count recovered, and suddenly I was free to sneak in a couple of meals with Angela at, God forbid, public restaurants rather than have to hide at home. I could actually eat food made in a kitchen that I couldn't see.

It was a chemo vacation.

Angela: Walt and I went on several dates, moments of freedom and happiness, albeit tinged with awareness that the hiatus would soon reach its end. Once during the mini-holiday, we drove to a hidden state park two hours north of Seattle, where we snowshoed on a pristine, tree-lined back trail for two hours, almost in defiance of the leukemia. And, of course, we hit McDonald's on the way back home.

The day after our snowshoeing escape, Angela called me over to the dining-room table where she was reading the *New York Times*.

"You should check this out."

"What?" I said flatly, grumpy from too much coffee, which I've since quit multiple times.

"This guy is a survivor," she said.

It turned out that a man named James Chippendale, an entrepreneur and successful concert manager about my age from Austin, Texas, had undergone a transplant ten years earlier. His match had been a grandfather living in a village of 150 people, two hours west of Berlin. After his transplant, James founded a nonprofit dedicated to building leukemia awareness and motivating people to register as bone marrow donors.[32] James also flew to Germany to find his donor and, after meeting him in the rural village where he lived, paid off the mortgage on the man's house and bought the property across the street for the man's son and daughter-in-law.

Not sure I can afford a thank-you gift like that...

I emailed James to ask for advice on my upcoming transplant, and we ended up speaking over the phone for a few minutes as I paced outside of the SCCA's entrance one sunny morning. It felt good to connect with someone who had traversed the path upon which I was embarking. My transplant loomed but a week away.

James told me to rinse with salt water at least once an hour while undergoing the transplant to defer the inevitable and painful breakdown of mouth tissue. I took him at his word and, later when I was ensconced in the hospital undergoing transplant, I swished salt water obsessively. I don't know if it helped, but I wasn't going to risk otherwise.

What happens in a stem cell transplant? Doctors use mega-watt chemo and hardcore radiation to nuke a patient's malfunctioning blood cell factory along with the zillions of nasty leukemic blasts coursing through

---

32   Love Hope Strength Foundation: www.lovehopestrength.org.

the patient's blood. They then introduce into the body a brand new blood cell factory, one donated by a genetically congruent relative or stranger. Or they take out the patient's own factory, hammer out the bad stuff, and put it back in to grow anew. Sometimes patients get stem cells extracted from donated umbilical cord blood.

Whatever the source of the healthy marrow, the goal is for it to take root and reboot the blood system.

One afternoon I explained leukemia to Luke, still only five years old. "Our blood is made up of a bunch of cells," I said as I drew several hollow discs "floating" inside the blood vessels of the human silhouette I had sketched clumsily on a sheet of printer paper. "Some of Daddy's blood cells are broken and the broken ones keep multiplying. They don't know to stop, so there are more and more and more of them. There are so many of the broken ones that there's no room left for the good ones! The doctors are going to use special medicine to get rid of all the broken ones in Daddy's blood so that the good ones have space to survive!"

Luke listened passively, looking down as he played with Legos. Not a word, but I knew he had absorbed the information.

A week later at the SCCA, a kindhearted child specialist brought Luke, Angela, and me into a conference room where a toy bone rested atop a round wooden table. The bone, aka the specialist's leukemia demo kit for kids—was filled with Red Hots[33] and white miniature marshmallows.

The young blonde assistant spent a good twenty minutes gently walking Luke through the story of blood cells, leukemia, and transplants. And when she was finished, she paused to ask Luke whether he had any questions. Luke, who had been doing his best to listen, had one.

"Why are we talking about this? Daddy already explained this to me," he said politely in his small voice.

Luke wasn't being a know-it-all. That's not him. He was just an honest, straight-shooting kid stating the facts.

How anticlimactic for that poor woman.

Angela: I felt the urgent need to help this young, well-meaning social worker save face. She had invested so much time in her story—and had seemed so excited to hear Luke's response. "Luke, like we talked about, Daddy is very sick," I interjected, "and he has to go to the hospital for a few weeks to get better. We just wanted to make sure you knew what was happening." Still polite, Luke said looking at me, "Well, you're not going anywhere are you?"

"No, sweetheart."

---

33   For those who didn't grow up in the US, Red Hots are small, round, spicy red hard candies. A well-played physical metaphor for red blood cells.

LUMBAR PUNCTURES

Throughout my treatment leading up to transplant, most chemo made its way into my blood via the Hickman line still hanging from my upper chest. But it went *only* into my blood. I also needed chemo in my spinal fluid, "intrathecal chemo," as it's called. Even though the leukemia wasn't in my spinal fluid at the time, the intrathecal injections were required nonetheless as a precaution.

"I need you to roll on your side and hug your knees," Dr. Austin told me as I lay on an exam bed in her Overlake clinic.

Following instructions, I hugged my knees and rolled over on my side. Dr. Austin began fingering the spaces between my vertebrae, searching for the right spot to insert a needle. When she found it, she marked it with her index finger and guided the needle into place. It set off electric jolts as it touched nerve endings en route to the spinal sac. And then I felt the "pop" when she pushed it through. With the needle now piercing the spine's protective membrane, she removed fluid to make room for an injection of methotrexate.

Call me a wimp, but let's just say I didn't love intrathecal injections. I did not "heart" or "lol" the needle-in-the-spine thing.

My most colorful experience with intrathecal chemo unfolded one morning in a sparsely equipped, lightless room in the basement of the University of Washington

Medical Center. There, as I lay face down on a long metal table, a young physician stared intently at an overhead monitor broadcasting a live, bright, glowing green x-ray of my back, as he puzzled over what to do next.

An abscess wound remained open on the surface of my lower back at the exact spot where the intrathecal needle was supposed to enter, one of five gashes still open from pus excavation after the E. coli infection that had left me unconscious for two weeks not long before. Concerned that sticking a needle into the exposed, raw tissue would risk infection and therefore wanting to take extra precaution, the SCCA had decided to send me to the University of Washington for a more high-tech approach to intrathecal. Laser-guided, if you will.

The glowing green monitor? It was a Google Map of the inside of my back, and the young physician was trying to figure out where to start his trip. Insert the needle here? There? How does he avoid the open crater? Having gained enough confidence to act, the doctor sent the needle in. *Ouch.* But only tentatively. Then out it came. Back in. Out… then in. Each time pushing further toward the spinal sac, as if the needle were feeling its way through the dark. Finally, after several failed attempts, my well-intentioned caretaker surrendered and called in a more senior physician to help. So now there were two doctors staring at the map as they conferred in low tones.

The senior physician eventually perforated the spinal sac (*pop!*) and started to attempt pulling out fluid with the syringe to make room for the methotrexate. Unfortunately, nothing came out—at least not at a measurable pace.

"Grab the top of the table," the young physician instructed me. I reached my arms forward to grasp the front metal edge as he raised the table to a steep angle. His goal? To see if gravity would speed the outflow of spinal fluid. It didn't. The fluid still dripped at an achingly slow pace as my knuckles grew white trying to keep myself from descending what had now become a playground slide.

Over time, my chemo regimen called for a total of six intrathecal treatments. I dreaded each one, in part because I wasn't a big fan of the stick-a-needle-in-my-back-and-puncture-the-spinal-sac thing, and in part because the treatments left me with resoundingly debilitating headaches due to the resulting imbalance in spinal fluid. No standing, no sitting. I was forced to lie flat for hours, the only way to alleviate the pain.

"We could try a caffeine bolus," suggested Jennifer, a nurse at the SCCA. "It's an infusion of concentrated caffeine known to rid patients of severe headaches. Another option would be a blood patch. You see, the spinal sac will sometimes leak fluid through the puncture made by the needle, leaving you short, ergo the headaches. A blood patch is exactly what it sounds like: the injection of a splotch of blood into the hole left by the needle in the spinal sac that coagulates, forming a plug that prevents additional spinal fluid from leaking. No more headaches."

"Let's give the caffeine a try first."

I checked into the SCCA at 7 p.m. that night for the caffeine bolus. The floor nurse placed me in a bed, connected an IV line to my Hickman, and opened the faucet. The caffeine flowed, a clear liquid, not brown like espresso, as one might imagine (although that would be cool—a doppio espresso draining directly into the heart).

Unfortunately, the bolus didn't work. The headache persisted.

One day remained before my transplant. And I didn't want to spend my time in the transplant ward trapped on my back thanks to headaches. So I opted for the blood patch, which ended up being administered at the University of Washington Medical Center's Pain Clinic.

There, the clinic's director went to work on my hand with a needle in an effort to draw fresh blood for the patch. He stabbed the flesh covering the metacarpals five times, *digging* vigorously under the skin. You'd think he would have given up after the third try, but no. Honestly, God bless the man, but I think his ego was in the way. He couldn't admit defeat, so the torment at the Pain Clinic proceeded unabated. That is until the director finally relinquished and, with chin still held high, called over a nurse, who got it on the first try.

No snarkiness here. Just comedy.

PARENTAL GUIDANCE

I had no idea what to expect from the stem cell

transplant that was rapidly approaching. Would it leave me debilitated? *Dead?*

Taking a cue from Sara (whose story I shared earlier), I decided to make videos for my kids—one for Luke and one for Sofia. In case I died or became debilitated, I wanted to leave them with parental guidance they could watch as they grew older. Guidance I could still give while relatively healthy, functioning, and conscious. A lifetime of parenting compressed into twenty-minute digital recordings.

A friend loaned me a video camera, which I placed on top of a tripod at one end of a spare room in our basement. I focused the lens on a chair at the other end of the room, clicked the Record button, and took a seat. Wearing a drab, olive green North Face fleece, I looked up at the camera lens, cleared my throat, and looked down at the notes I had handwritten. My talking points, if you will. I was delivering a presentation. Sure, this was love—and my audience a two- and a five-year-old—but it was also business. I had important things to land. Wisdom to impart. I wasn't going to wing it.

Luke's video came first. I spoke to the camera as if it were Luke himself.

"Luke, the doctors tried really, really hard to make me better, but unfortunately, in the end, they couldn't save me..."

The videos actually still exist, although I've never watched them. In fact, I only happened upon the mini-

DVR tapes the other day. There's nothing psychologically keeping me from watching them. I just haven't made the time.

PREPPING FOR MORE FUN

Sitting in a tiny room in the basement of the UW Medical Center, I noticed the fluorescent light made the white brick walls look as if they were made of baby powder.

"Do you have any questions?" asked the nurse, who sat on a stool inches away from me. She had just spent half an hour walking me through the intricacies of the full-body radiation I was about to undergo. Because my chair was lower than her stool, I had kept my neck craned the entire time to maintain eye contact.

The story? The next day I would begin a three-day regimen of radiation wipeouts, one treatment each morning, one each afternoon. Together these were aimed at annihilating all white blood cells in my body, including the marauding blasts, thereby making way for the stem cells coming from my donor to situate themselves.

"No, it all makes sense," I replied. Another day, another procedure.

"Some men freeze sperm before the radiation given that the treatment renders them sterile," she explained. "Is this something you'd like to do?"

I didn't have to think about the answer. "No, thanks."

Angela and I were good with the two we had. Both working professionals, we had just enough time in the week to do an okay job with Luke and Sofia. I know some parents can pull off more than two children. Theoretically we probably could, as well, but it'd take organizational discipline not necessarily abundant in our home. We had already given away our dogs since we more or less neglected them after having Luke and Sofia—though probably the bigger reason was that they were both insane.

"OK, then. Let's head next door."

I followed the nurse as she led me into the hall and through a pair of tall swinging doors, not unlike the entrance to a restaurant kitchen.

"How are you feeling, Mr. Harp?" asked the waiting technician, his angular nose barely buttressing his glasses.

"Good, thanks."

The two of us stared at each other for a moment. Neither spoke.

What am I doing here?

"We're not going to run you through any treatments today," the technician finally allowed. "I'm just going to take some measurements."

"OK."

I waited for the tech to say something else, but he seemed hesitant.

"Did Melissa tell you about the test?"

"Um...no." The nurse hadn't mentioned any test. I had no idea what he was talking about.

Realizing I hadn't been duly briefed, the tech sheepishly apologized and retreated backward through the swinging doors. A few seconds later, the nurse from the tiny office with the stool walked back in.

"Mr. Harp, leukemic cells tend to congregate in the testes," she explained. "It's a safe haven for them. So as part of your total body radiation, we will need to apply a 'testis boost' to your groin. Think of it as an extra shot of radiation for good measure."

I smiled politely. The whole thing seemed pretty straightforward.

The other guy couldn't tell me this?

The technician returned and asked me to lie down on the plastic sled connected to an MRI machine that seemed small given the vastness of the room.

"OK, Mr. Harp, I'm going to need you to take down your pants so I can perform a quick test."

"What's the test?" I asked, a little confused, unbuckling my belt and sliding the waist of my jeans and boxers down to my heels, all of which would have been much easier to do standing up.

"I need to measure your scrotum."

Feeling a little helpless now that I had bound my ankles with bunched denims, I watched as the tech busied himself with something on a nearby table. When he turned around, his index finger and thumb were pinching what looked like a stack of cocktail coasters. "Comin' attcha!" he said as he reached between my legs with one of the discs, which I noticed was marked with three thick, black concentric circles, crossed by two perpendicular lines, perhaps drawn with a Sharpie. It was exactly what you'd see when looking the scope of a high-powered rifle.

"What size do you think you are?" the tech asked, standing upright, returning the coaster to the stack in his hand. "Some men are small, others medium or large."

Self-aware and humble enough to know I probably wasn't large, I wanted to believe that I wasn't small either. "Medium?" I said with slight uncertainty. The tech placed another of the translucent circles on the pouch of skin housing my testicles before pulling it away. Then, without hesitating, he lowered another and, after a barely perceptible pause, pulled away, satisfied.

"Pants up!" he said cheerfully.

I pulled my boxers back up, my cheeks flushed.

Better not ask him what size I am. I don't want to risk hearing that I'm small.

The morning after the scrotum size-up, I returned to the UWMC and its basement for the inaugural round of radiation. There I swapped my street clothes for a faded green cotton gown and waited to be called in. Soon, a female technician, a good ten years younger than I was, with long, shiny black hair pulled into a ponytail, came for me. Her charming smile showed flawless white enamel. Together we walked up a curved ramp and into a brightly lit room. Once inside, the tech pointed to a tall, black metal cage that if covered with wood could be used as a wardrobe. Attached to a bar that crossed the middle of the cage was a bike seat. I was directed to rest my hindquarters on this perch, standing with legs slightly bent. I held this pose for fifteen minutes facing forward and another fifteen minutes facing backward while a radiation machine at the far end of the room soundlessly bathed me in atomic particles.

A surprise awaited me when it came time to turn around so that the radiation could penetrate me from the back. There on the wall in front of my face, someone had thoughtfully taped a black-and-white twenty-four by twenty-four inch Where's Waldo? poster. So I kept myself occupied for the ensuing thirty minutes searching for Waldo in the hilly village where he hid among the hundreds of other tiny characters. Nutty, Waldo!

"You ready?" asked the tech.

"Yep."

"Want some music? We use Pandora, so I can create any station you want."

"U2 would be great."

The technician picked up an iPhone, kindly set the Pandora station to U2, and placed it into a speaker dock before leaving the room. As she exited, a massive metal door slid shut. It sounded like a bank vault closing.

The Edge, Bono, Waldo, and me naked on a bike seat that had been welded onto a metal cage. Photons, electrons—whatever the subatomic particles were—scattered around and through me, while the sweet young technician with the beatific smile and her cohorts kept watch via closed-circuit TV safely in a small room outside the giant lead door.

The next day, anticipating that I'd probably grow weary of Waldo, I brought my own entertainment, an audiobook of *When You Are Engulfed in Flames* by David Sedaris. I love Sedaris' writing—it's truly laugh-out-loud—but I was surprised by the number of f-bombs he dropped in this particular work. Self-conscious about f-this and fi-that, I asked a tech who had entered the room during intermission whether she was offended.

"Of course not," she laughed. "We're all cracking up back there!"

Whew!

I expected to feel ill from the radiation, but really I just felt exhausted. Very, very exhausted. So much so that I rented a hotel room by the medical center on the morning of the second day so I could sleep in advance of the evening session rather than spend time driving home and back. Nausea must have been lurking, though. As I walked down the ramp after the third morning of radiation, warm saliva spilled into my mouth. A garbage can at the bottom of the ramp caught virtually all the vomit that streamed from my gut. It was quite serendipitous, actually.

"How're you feeling?" my mom asked me later that morning at brunch. Bravely, the two of us had ventured to a local pancake house. My white blood cell count had yet to fall from the radiation, so we figured I'd be safe from any bacteria introduced by the restaurant's kitchen. And despite vomiting that morning, I didn't feel nauseous. In fact, with an empty stomach, I had a pretty good appetite.

"Are you nervous?" my mom asked.

"Maybe a little," I said. "Though really I'm just going through the motions." Which I was. Treatment to treatment. Like an automatic car wash.

The next day, Angela and I drove back to the UW Medical Center to check into the eighth floor of the Pacific Tower— the transplant ward. Had I not known otherwise, the ward could have housed patients with any variety of illnesses. Nothing there screamed "transplant."

Upon my first step onto the ward's worn laminate tile, the stopwatch started. Countdown to thirty days. In the brig. And if what I had read held true, it wasn't going to be fun. "This will be the most difficult thing you've ever done," Dr. Austin had warned. So I was braced for the worst. For one thing, I expected that within a few days my mouth would be overcome with raw sores, making it impossible to eat and resulting in the need for doctors to stick a feeding tube into my nose or stomach or wherever it goes. I also anticipated reaching the point where I would be generating so much mucus in my mouth that I would no longer be able to speak, forced to expectorate globs of goo second after second. It's what happened to Richard, after all. Severe mucositis.

Angela and I checked in at the front desk. Soon, a tall, heavy-set nurse in his mid-fifties approached. "Follow me," he said unceremoniously, as if bored with life—or at least his job.

Probably counting the days until retirement.

The nurse walked us to one of approximately two dozen rooms on the floor, the hallway of which formed a capital "A." With my gown on and my vitals checked, I sat at a small table—the one and only in the room—across from Angela, who'd wisely brought a Scrabble board with her.

"Shall we play?" she asked cheerfully.

"Sure."

Thus began stem cell transplant day one. It kicked off with yet another napalming of my immune system, should in fact any elements have remained after the flood of radiation. Nurses plied me with enough chemo to denude a planet, the immediate effect of which was...nothing— at least in terms of side effects. Chemo creeps up over a period of days; it doesn't strike like a falling anvil.

I created a simple line graph in an Excel spreadsheet so I could track my white blood cell count over the ensuing days. I expected the line to drop precipitously to zero as chemo went about killing any cells that remained, then hold flat for several days, and, if all went well, slowly rise once the donor stem cells took root and started producing a new blood system. God forbid the line never climbed. That would mean the stem cells hadn't grafted. And I would be left with no immune system.[34]

The red line on the graph—my white cell tracker—fell off a cliff within a few days, hit the horizontal x-axis, and flatlined.

Time to bring on the stem cells.

Time for my "new birthday," as they call it: March 10, 2009.

The same nurse who had brought me to my room on day one came in the afternoon of the big day. Ironic that the bored old nurse would administer the life-saving miracle, but he rose to the occasion. There was a pleasantness about him—a hint of anticipation, even.

I like this guy.

He let me know that the donor's stem cells would soon arrive from the other side of the state.

"What happens if a donor decides to back out at the last minute?" I asked.

"Donors don't renege," he replied, his nose scrunched as he read the stats on the vitals monitor. "And here's an

---

34   I haven't Googled yet what would happen next, but I can probably guess.

interesting fact for you...do you remember when all air traffic was halted during 9/11?"

"Sure..."

"Well, flights containing stem cells for transplants were still allowed to fly."

Later that evening, the nurse returned carrying a clear plastic parcel the size of a snack-sized bag of Doritos. Instead of nacho cheese-flavored corn chips, an orange-red slush filled the package—the donor's stem cells. This was the moment. The big thing. Fluorescent lights in the ceiling reflecting off of the cloud layer outside the window cast the room in silver. Angela sat next to me, lying passively on the hospital bed, which was inclined at a forty-five-degree angle. As bland and non-festive as the room was, it was an event.

"I'm going to give you some Benadryl in case your body reacts negatively to the stem cells," the nurse told me. Very well. He might as well have given me three shots of vodka, as the Benadryl left me slurring my words. The life-saving smoothie, a second chance at life, dripped from the bag into the Hickman line into my heart, where the donor's cells were propelled through my circulatory system.

No balloons or confetti fell from the ceiling, no fanfare erupted, no cake with candles appeared. Yet still I was undergoing rebirth. This simple sad, quiet setting was the scene of my new chance at life.

Speaking of new, with the infusion of stem cells, my

blood type changed from type A negative to type O. *Kapow*. It was, in fact, no longer my blood system—I now had my donor's, although I wouldn't know his name for a year.

The day following my auspicious new birthday began as any other. The stem cells hadn't altered my reality—I didn't feel different. I couldn't sense some cosmic force working inside me. It was just another day.

Yet, unseen, magic did indeed unfold.

I don't do well with unstructured time. I was looking at as much as a month stuck idle in a small hospital room ensconced in a quiet, isolated tower with nothing to do. So to keep my days—and my sanity—from dissolving into mush, I wrote out a daily schedule in a spreadsheet: up at 7 a.m., breakfast, morning walk, morning read, lunch, afternoon walk, and so on. I knew that without a regimen, I would end up sleeping all the time, and eventually become listless and depressed.

Angela: I visited Walt every day without fail. The highlight was always a game or two of Scrabble. Helped pass the time, else he was walking the halls or dozing and I was on email with work. At first, I felt bad leaving him at night. It was as if I was leaving him in a jail cell. But one night, he said to me, "This is like when we worked in the Senate and you visited me every day in the mail room..."

That's when I knew it would be ok.

I purposely avoided the bed as much as possible—I knew that lying around and sleeping would result in a vicious downward cycle. So I walked quite a bit, which the staff encouraged. A map on the wall marked the distance of the hallways, which, as I shared earlier, formed a giant A. I decided to walk a mile a day. Thus, with my IV pole in tow, the bags of chemo and hydration swinging from the crossbar, I walked the A at least twice a day.

I encountered very few patients in the halls. Most patients on the floor were bedridden, and the ones I did come across were a good three or more decades my senior. While we smiled when we passed, per the ward's unspoken protocol, we said nothing. Just a nod and a smile. At most. And we were sure to stay to one side of the hallway so as to allow plenty of room for our respective IV trees to pass. The IV pole of one woman I encountered held not one crossbar, but two, both laden with swaying bags of medication.

She must really be sick.

Believe it or not, I actually called the transplant ward a couple of weeks before my arrival date to ask whether I could bring an exercise bike into my room, wanting to make sure I had something to do to pass the time and keep active. Oddly enough, the answer was: "We already have one on the floor." And that they surely did. An old stationary bike rested against the side of the wall on the A's left side. I didn't touch it, though. I didn't even get close. Dusty and outdated, it wasn't very inviting. And I wasn't exactly brimming with energy. Instead, I would pass by the bike on my laps around the A and pause at a nearby window where I could look out at the massive University of Washington football stadium. Rising high a few hundred yards away, the structure was abutted by an expansive asphalt parking lot where tiny cars came and went like ladybugs.

Unlike in this ward, life is happening down there.

The A's crossbar housed the ward's ICU. When walking there, I tried not to stare through the windows, but I couldn't help but look. Person after person lay motionless in bed with a clear CPAP mask covering his or her face to combat the acute respiratory failure brought on by infection amid lack of immune defense.[35]

The people trapped in these rooms were mercifully unconscious and therefore unaware of their circumstances. Fuck...at least I could have visitors and walk around. And I didn't have a mask smothering my face.

Angela: While Walt was on the ward, a tempest in a teacup stirred at home. I truly love and respect Walt's mother. I'd go so far

---

35   Per the National Heart, Lung, and Blood Institute: "CPAP, or continuous positive airway pressure, is a treatment that uses mild air pressure to keep the airways open. See www.nhlbi.nih.gov.

as to say we are close. A week or so into the transplant, though, the tension hit a tipping point. Too much stress. Sharon ended up moving out of the guest room to live in SCCA-owned housing. She and I split days and evenings so that each of us could have time with Walt yet also have breathing room.

Sticking with my self-prescribed regimen, I got out of bed each morning at 7 a.m. and ordered breakfast, which I'd eat at the small square table set against the window, the table where Angela and I played Scrabble. Without fail, never more than a few minutes after my breakfast had arrived, a line of young medical students, all decked out in pristine lab coats, would walk into my room single file and stand in a military line facing me across the room from where I sat. The attending physician, slender with white hair, led this spectral troop. But rather than stand alongside the students, he would inevitably saunter over to where I was sitting, hands behind his back, lean over, and smile at me. And that's it. No words. He just stared at me. Head cocked to the side. Not quite a crazy look in his eye, but in a movie there would have been. Naturally, I felt compelled to break the silence, so every morning I gave a big hello to everyone, both the attending and his entourage.

"Good morning!" I greeted them, not with gusto, but with a "this is awkward so I'm going to speak loudly" kind of volume.

"I see you have an appetite," the attending remarked, looking back and forth between me and the French toast on my tray.

"Yup! Eating just fine," I replied, for some reason feeling compelled to sound robust.

Silence...

I looked up at the doctor and smiled.

"OK," he said. Then, after yet another strange expanse of silence, he exited the room, the wordless queue of students trailing behind him. No "Goodbye!" or "Looking great!" or "See you tomorrow." Just odd, unapologetic silence.

It would happen again the next day—pretty much word for word, action by action.

I kid you not.

Asperger's syndrome—both the doctor and the students?

Midway through my time on the ward, Angela and Tara—a lovely, lovely person and friend of mine from work—orchestrated a mail campaign asking thirty people who knew me from various stages in my life to write a letter recalling a memory of me. I drank the stories like honey wine, each thoughtful, clever, wistful, and heartwarming. I limited myself to reading only one per day. I didn't want to burn through them all at once and have nothing to look forward to after that. It was going to be a long stay on the ward—I needed to stretch 'em out.

The letters? About the best gift *ever*—a neat thing to

consider if you know anyone facing a long hospital stay or recovery at home, or simply needing a pick-me-up.

Meanwhile, the lonely line on the Excel spreadsheet, the one tracking my white blood cell count, inched forward flat against the x-axis. Meaning at zero. For six days. No grafting, no white blood cells, no immune system to ward off invaders. A virulent fungal, bacterial, or viral agent would have most likely killed me, putting me in the third piece of the pie chart I had sketched while sitting with Dr. Harrison.

"And if the line on your Excel graph doesn't fee fah foo..."

Then the line ticked up.

"It's happened, Walt. Your WBC—white blood cell count—showed point two today!" said Terry, the physician assistant on duty. Hands on his hips, he stared at me expectantly. "You've grafted!"

I have to admit it didn't feel like an occasion. No doubt that's how it would be portrayed in a Hollywood film—fireworks, tears, rock ballad. But I hadn't been worried over whether the new stem cells would actually graft. Maybe there was a fleeting question, but for the most part, this was all just another procedure. Another mile in the marathon. And, honestly, I take things for granted, which is both a strength and a weakness. Sometimes it's good not to sweat stuff—sometimes it isn't. That said, as a nerd locked in a tower with not much else to distract me, I was excited to see the line in the graph tick upwards.

Cool!

Terry moved to write ".2" on the whiteboard facing my bed while also erasing the "7" that was there and replacing it with the number "8" to represent the new post-transplant day count. While I was always glad to see the count rise by an increment of one, the pace couldn't have moved more slowly. *7...8...9...* I was intent on getting discharged as early as possible. I didn't want to wait the full thirty days I had been told to plan on. I wanted out *sooner.*

When day thirteen arrived, my stomach decided to no longer accept food. A single bite of oatmeal brought up the entire contents of my digestive system. Fortunately, the internal food protest lasted only three days. I was able to get down a few saltine crackers on the fourth. Apart from that, though, I was gliding through the transplant without incident. Odd...When was the hammer going to fall? Where was the feeding tube? Wasn't this supposed to be the hardest thing I'd ever been through?

Don't let me kid you. I *knew* I was lucky. I didn't take my situation for granted. I certainly recalled that when Richard reached the second week of transplant, his mouth was so full of mucus he couldn't speak. Further, as my leukemia story unfolded, so did that of a Pilates instructor who taught at a studio near our house on Mercer Island. Young, fit, and beautiful, with flowing black hair and slender wrists, she had contracted the disease two months before I had. As I slid through my transplant, chemo laid siege to her once athletic body, forcing her to the hospital again and again. No respite. No extended break at home with her husband and children. Just emergency after emergency after emergency, including one when her husband rushed her in after her eye swelled to the size of a golf ball.

Except for the time when she wrote on her blog of the joy of being able to take a bath, she never really got a chance to come up for air before she passed and left her husband and small children behind.

Terry walked into my room on day eighteen with a noticeable bounce in his step.

"We're going to discharge you today!" he announced, looking first at me and then at Angela, who had been engrossed in email on her phone and now stood up, hurried around the table, and kissed me on the cheek. "What time?" she asked excitedly.

"We'll have Walt out of here by 3 p.m. I'll start on the paperwork now."

Terry left the room. A minute later Angela leaned over and whispered to me, "I think we need to say something about the kids."

"That they just got over a bug?" I asked.

"Yes."

"Why? I can avoid them by staying in the basement. Why would you bring that up?"

"Given your susceptibility to infection, I think it's essential that we let Terry know. I don't want you back here—God forbid in the ICU."

"Seriously?"

"Yes, Walt. Seriously!" Perturbed, she stood and walked out of the room, only to return, a grim expression on her face.

"Terry's concerned about the risk of infection from the kids at home," she told me. "He said he needs to confer with the attending physician before deciding whether to discharge you."

Crap. They're going to change their minds...

I got out of bed and picked up the maroon box engraved with the word "Scrabble" in italicized gold letters from the counter where it rested. Angela and I sat across from each other at the now too-familiar square table adjacent to the window, an oyster-colored cloud layer suspended low outside. We needed distraction, so we began to lay the small wooden tiles one by one on the cardboard game board pocked with pink and blue squares that read "Double Word Score" and "Triple Letter Score."

Forty-five minutes passed quickly.

"I win," I announced, having beaten Angela by pure chance (definitely not superior skill). It frustrated Angela that I won despite having chemo-brain.

"Have you seen where the saltines went?" I asked,

stretching my arms while looking up at the tiled ceiling.

Angela's attention had returned to her email. "On the counter." A semi-opaque package of the thin baked salted squares rested under the sanitizer dispenser on the far side of the room. I walked over to retrieve them but at the last minute veered into the bathroom and closed the door behind me. When I stepped back into the room minutes later, I saw Terry standing with Angela by the window.

Terry turned to look at me. "Guys, I talked to the attending physician. He's concerned about the risk of infection at home. We need to keep you here a few more days."

Angela's face sank.

"Are you ok?" Terry asked.

"No." She paused, her composure cracking. "I thought we were going home."

I interjected. "What? It's as likely—if not *more* likely—the hospital could make me sick. And it's not the hospital's role to 'protect' me outside of the hospital."

"OK," Terry replied, clearly surprised by Angela's tears and reddening face. "I hear you. Let me go talk to the attending again."

Terry left the room only to return a moment later. No suspenseful pause. He was on a mission.

"Looks like you're going home, Walt," he told us. Angela immediately brightened. "You will, though, need to be very careful. Your immune system is that of a newborn. It knows nothing. It recognizes nothing. And, as such, it is incredibly delicate."

"Thanks, Terry. We really appreciate it," I said.

"Yes, thank you," added Angela, now smiling.

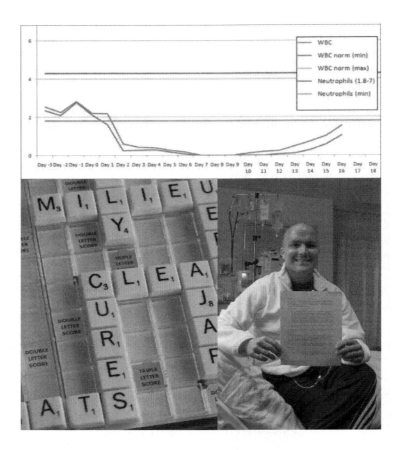

Above: My Excel tracker shows my white blood cell count grafted and rising.

Below left: Scrabble—the transplant pastime of choice for Angela, me, and my mother.

Below right: Reading the first of the letters from the writing campaign Angela and Tara organized.

Angela on receiving news that I was getting released from the transplant ward after eighteen days there (March 2011).

WELCOME HOME, DADDY!

Several small sheets of white paper hung from a long piece of twine strung over the front door. Upon each was hand-painted a blue letter that when combined read "Welcome Home Daddy!" The kids and our nanny had been at work. I smiled at the banner, but couldn't help but feel anxious the moment I walked into the house. The staff in the transplant ward had left me on edge. *Infection, infection, infection...you don't want to go back there...*

I really didn't. So I smiled and said a warm hello and blew kisses to my sweet Luke and Sofia, who stood peering at me through the vertical iron bars of the stair rail, and then walked down to the basement, where the charcoal dusk gave the room the feel of a dead tanker on the ocean floor. And there I remained for three days. I mostly spent them sleeping, because I was completely wiped out—like never before—and fearful of venturing upstairs lest the kids, who had just recovered from colds, made me sick. I wasn't going back to the transplant ward. Wasn't going to the ICU on the crossbar of the A. Wasn't going to have a plastic CPAP mask cover my face.

Angela: I went downstairs to visit Walt every now and then, often just to bring him food, but we didn't sleep together. He didn't want to risk touching anyone, including me, so he spent much of those three days in a prone position on the couch, from which standing up, I noticed, took focused effort.

On the third night, I walked into the basement bedroom as Walt was getting ready to sleep, the one lamp filling the room with a romantic yellow glow.

"You ok?" I asked, though I could tell he wasn't. Walt looked lonely.

"Want me to sleep with you down here tonight?" I offered.

She's not sick. Could it really be that much of a risk? Whatever. I don't care.

"That would be nice."

The anxiety that had built up over the preceding seventy-two hours drained from my body the moment we pulled together under the covers.

I eventually moved upstairs but still napped in the basement every day, lulled by the hum of the whirring furnace, which I kept turned up despite the warm May weather since the transplant had left me feeling strangely cold. I would often awake to the buzz of gardeners mowing our neighbors' lawn, a sound I grew to hate as it reminded me of where I was—stuck in my basement, drained of strength and energy, unable to risk going out in the world. I resented the flowering trees and bushes outside; it was all so manicured and the spring sun only made me feel loathsome.

Fucking suburbia.

I found myself looking forward to the days when I was scheduled for follow-up appointments at the SCCA. In the months leading up to transplant—and during the transplant itself—I was constantly surrounded by doctors, nurses, family, and friends. I was rarely alone, and there was always something to do. Checking into the hospital and getting chemo was something to do. Not that I looked forward to it. But when I was there, the staff kept me company and the routine occupied my mind. At home, I was *preoccupied*, left alone to finally absorb the true gravity of what had happened to me and what I still faced. It took the stillness, silence, and isolation for it all to sink in. I perseverated endlessly over the possibility of relapse, particularly in light of the odds cited by Dr. Harrison and the brief from UpToDate.com as well as Richard's haunting story.

I marked off each day on a gardening calendar given to us by Angela's aunt, a botanist. One hundred was the magic number. Research physicians had concluded that transplant patients needed to stay under the close watch of the SCCA for one hundred days before venturing back out into the world, and even then only cautiously.

It might as well have been one hundred years. It felt impossibly long. The calendar stared back at me with rows of stark, empty squares stretching across the pages of March through June, a picture of a different garden on each one.

It's going to take forever to cross off one hundred days!

I marked the time with daily walks. I'd start out by weaving through the neighborhood, then turn onto a particular dirt path bordered by tall grass. The trail opened to an expansive view of Boeing Field and the surrounding housing developments, spread like an urban meadow on the other side of the water opposite Mercer Island. To the south of the island, the mammoth Mount Rainier rose in enormity while the snow-frosted Cascade mountain range and the black-green foothills that preceded them stretched across the horizon to the east.

There I would come to pause and reflect.

These mountains will be here long after I'm gone. People come and go. The mountains will simply remain. Unassailable. Indifferent.

The vista left me feeling wistful and insignificant.

I seldom watched TV, even though we had a new fifty-inch LCD in the basement, complete with surround sound (which I had never taken the time to figure out how to make work properly). Other than bouts of graphically violent mixed martial arts, though, nothing on TV could distract me. My mind was forever racing, unable to free itself of disquietude.

I once tried to watch *American Idol*, which Angela loves (and, yes, I like as well). I'm ashamed to admit it, but I felt a little bitter watching the young, radiant contestants chase their dreams, free to fly while my life had face-planted into the dirt.

MTV showed a compelling documentary about a young AIDS activist who ultimately succumbed to the illness. Over a period of weeks, the vivacious twenty-something went from a vibrant community leader and AIDS awareness advocate to a starkly silent, emaciated wraith in a wheelchair with an IV pole hanging off the back. He finally died in his sleep, gasping for air. I couldn't pull myself away from witnessing yet another true story with a terrible ending. Another frightening, indelible entry into my mental library of "that could be me."

Books did a decent job of diverting my thoughts. I read one by actor Michael J. Fox, who came down with Parkinson's disease and who stated in the book that he wasn't one to get depressed, despite his disease. Given my malaise, I was envious.

I wish I wasn't depressed.

Another book described how a handful of individuals went about their lives despite having to deal with debilitating, progressively crippling, or even terminal diseases. The challenges I faced were nothing compared to theirs.

Why did I read these kinds of things? Well, the people in the stories...they felt like company, almost. Reading their narratives gave me solace. They told me I wasn't alone in dealing with illness.

At night, I scrolled through I Can Has Cheezburger?

(icanhascheezburger.com) and the associated Fail Blog (failblog.cheezburger.com). Yes, pictures of adorable dogs and cats tagged with funny captions and videos of skateboarders crashing into walls took me away. Reading email from work that trickled passively into my in-box, mostly broad announcements rather than personal communications, made me feel as if the world was passing me by. Once, my team's general manager unknowingly—or perhaps knowingly—lifted my spirits when he commented in an email that, "Walter can tackle that when he's back," reinforcing that I still counted.

Outside the confines of my basement, meanwhile, the global financial crisis raged on. The US unemployment rate raced toward 10 percent as a tidal wave of home foreclosures surged. Adding to the dreariness, the PBS news show *Frontline* aired a documentary about the state of health care in the US, making poignant the differences in options for the haves and have-nots. I shivered at the thought of needing to fundraise amid all of this hell to pay for a transplant, which some families are forced to do. And I blanch to this day at accounts of people who go bankrupt and even end up losing their homes in order to pay for vital care.

You are indeed fortunate.

The first time I found myself lying on the couch in the family room upstairs, where my children played and where energy filled the air, it became very clear to me how different life had become. I used to tease, chase, and tickle my kids nonstop. Now I didn't. I used to hold them aloft on my feet as I lay on my back so they could "fly." No energy for that, much less strength. Too young, Sofia didn't notice. However, at five years of age, Luke did. I remember him looking at me expectantly, yet hesitantly, as I lay motionless on the couch.

Maybe Dad will jump up and play with me, he must have thought. *Then again, maybe not. Something's wrong.* We had educated Luke about leukemia. The information hadn't fazed him in the slightest, but my inactivity did.

Angela: There was no question in my mind that the kids were affected by their father's physical state and emotional withdrawal. Mercifully, however, at ages five and two, they were young enough that they focused only on the present, not the "what if" scenarios of infection, graft-versus-host-disease, and relapse. Yes, with their Dad out of commission, they felt loss—but not fear of what might lay ahead.

In fact, my strength and any kind of endurance took forever to return. I was anything but my normal, energetic, driven self. It required all the energy I could muster just to clean up the McDonald's strawberry shake that Sofia had spilled in the back of the Subaru, something I volunteered to do, my first effort at asserting independence.

Then we decided to go for a hike. Why not? It was

gorgeous outside.

"Ange, I don't think we should go very far," I said as I stepped out of the car at the entrance to the Twin Falls Trail, still fifty pounds lighter than I had been pre-diagnosis. "It'd be great to walk all the way to the waterfalls, but if one of the kids poops out, I won't be able to carry them back."

With Sofia's hand in mine, and Luke's in Angela's, the four of us plodded slowly along the narrow dirt path that led into a verdant, heavily treed Northwest outback. Sofia was still so tiny that the top of her sunbonnet barely reached the back pocket of my jeans. We soon came upon another family standing on the rocks that bordered the Snoqualmie River. The father held his small daughter in the air with one arm as he helped her skip rocks across the water.

Ugh. That's what a dad is supposed to be. Strong.

Angela: Joan, Walt's primary nurse at the SCCA, had given him a long list of restrictions all post-transplant patients were to follow. She made it clear he was to strictly adhere to the rules, else risk life-threatening infection or GVHD. He couldn't sit on grass or go near dirt. No sun—he had to stay in the shade or stand covered in long sleeves despite the heat of approaching summer. No going out to eat. No 300 or ballgame with the kids. The list was extensive.

But I kept dragging him outside. Yes, he would sit miserable on a bench in the eighty-degree sunshine wearing jeans, a long-sleeve jersey, baseball hat, and sunglasses, his face, hands, and neck slathered in SPF 30, while the kids frolicked on play structures at the park. But at least he was outside.

I was also desperate to have my husband and partner back. It was becoming too much for me. I had spent six months sacrificing and fighting fear while managing the kids, the house, my job, the doctors. Despite enormous support from family and friends, I still felt utterly alone—that all the risk and work fell on my shoulders and if he died then I had everything to lose. I was running at 200 percent all the time and yet here he was. Still distant. A shell of his former self.

One morning I yelled at him. "You need to snap out of it and rejoin the family. I didn't work this hard to not have you back." Walt lashed back with something about how I was being hasty and it was no wonder I had fought with his mother.

"Then feel free to go live with your mother," I retorted. Not my shining moment to say the least, but my tank was on empty. I couldn't be the martyr anymore.

But there were signs of promise. The next day, Sofia, then just two and a half, became hysterical when she couldn't find the necklace of plastic pink pearls she always carried. Sofia has never been a great self-soother, and those pearls were a source of comfort for her. She was inconsolable.

As Sofia's yelling escalated into bellowing anger, I fell into helplessness and panic. So tired of having to do everything on my own. Thankfully, Walt wasn't miles away in a hospital bed. He was home. And when he saw our desperation, he volunteered to find the necklace. Minutes later, when he returned from the basement holding Sofia's pearls triumphantly overhead, I felt awash with relief. A rare moment of respite.

Things are going to be ok, I mused.

Walter's Bedside Blog

Life Post-transplant

Posted by Angela Lean on Wednesday 04/08/2009

Walt and I are on edge waiting for him to get his first post-transplant biopsy this afternoon. The results will tell us the status of the leukemia now that the donor cells have been in the mix beating up the old immune system for nearly 30 days. Medical science is amazing and we are both in awe of the incredible care and treatment Walt is receiving these days, but bottom line is that much of this is out of anyone's control and Lady Luck plays a huge role in these results.

*We are also learning the art of patience
here in the Lean/Harp household, watching
and waiting not only for good results
but also for Walt to recover and reclaim
his life bit by bit. Major milestones
include his first drive to the grocery
store, spending time with friends and the
kids, and our first date in months (lunch
yesterday at Bennett's). These highlights,
however, punctuate the other realities of
continued fatigue and the daily regimen
of meds and IV fluids. He continues to do
really well and I remain inspired by his
stamina and fortitude.*

*Next week signifies my return to work
after five weeks off. I look forward to
getting back into the swing of things but
am wistful over leaving the home front.
The mother of a friend of mine said that
"challenge builds character." We certainly
have plenty of character these days with
this challenge. We also have perspective
on what's most important—health, family,
and friends—and I certainly hope that none
of us take those for granted after all of
this.*

*Once again, please send all good thoughts,
prayers, and karma our way, encouraging
Lady Luck to be on our side.*

Cheers, Angela

As day one hundred finally approached, I emailed Roger,
my manager at Microsoft, to lay out plans for my return.
He had been covering my responsibilities for nearly five

months, in addition to the rest of his heavy workload. Taking an uncharacteristically conservative stance, I told Roger that rather than jump back in the pool I would start part-time at twenty hours per week on June 22 and gradually move to full-time—and that I wouldn't be able to travel. No way was I going to be stuck in an aluminum tube for hours sharing recycled air with a bunch of people coughing and sneezing. Not with my weakened immune system.

When I shared the plan over the phone, I thought I detected a note of frustration in Roger's voice. I had told him I was returning at the end of June. Now I needed more time?

"Scratch that. I'll be back *full-time* on the twenty-second."

Whether or not Roger had actually given pause or I was projecting out of guilt, I felt better the moment I returned to work. A miracle cure for angst and unhappiness. No kidding. I was regaining my life. My normal. How could I not be thrilled? Sure, my stamina wasn't great at first, but I got back into the groove. After a week, I was my old self.

Hiking with Sofia (age two and a half) on Twin Falls Trail just outside of Seattle. Sapped of all strength and energy by the recent transplant, I walked only a short distance. I was too afraid I wouldn't be able to carry her out if she tired (May 2009).

ACCIDENT

One more story for color before we ride off into the post-transplant sunset.

Before I went back to work, while I was still at home recovering from the transplant, my walks around the neighborhood grew longer and longer as my stamina gradually returned. A couple of weeks before the end of the one hundred days, I had almost finished a one-mile circle around the neighborhood when it came. The urgency. The urgency to poo that only a post-transplant patient who is prescribed seven zillion milligrams of magnesium oxide per day can experience.

I started an attempt at mind control. *Don't think about it. Walk slowly and hold your you-know-what tight!*

The urgency erupted into an emergency. I started walking as fast as I could for fear that running would unleash the Kraken.

I could see my house...but *damn! Still too far away.*

I had to give in. I couldn't hold on, a circumstance I had never found myself in despite a lifetime of walking, jogging, and hiking. Whenever I was out and about and had the sudden need to go, I had always made it home or to a store or, on the odd occasion, to the woods; yet not more than a fifty-yard dash to my front lawn, I could do nothing but let go.

And once it started, there was no stopping. A thick,

warm, non-potable smoothie ran down my legs, soiling entirely my favorite jeans.

Honestly, the thing I felt most—more than ghastliness— was sweet relief.

Mercifully back inside, I wore my jeans into the shower. I wasn't sure what else to do with them since I'd never crapped my jeans before. I decided I couldn't subject our washing machine to poo-saturated, adult-sized Banana Republic denims; the idea of remnant poo particles lingering in an appliance meant to keep our clothes, dish towels, and sheets sanitary didn't sit well with me. So, as endearing, worn, and comfortable as those jeans were, after the shower I stuffed them into a trash bag, tied it closed, and tossed it into the garbage.

Note to fellow transplant patients: watch out for magnesium oxide. You won't find the risk of poo-mergency in the literature!

THE GREATEST GIFT

The SCCA maintains anonymity for both the stem cell donor and recipient for one year, so it wasn't until almost exactly 365 days after my transplant that I received a handwritten card in the mail from a stranger, a high-school teacher and football coach named Matt, who months later visited me at my home while in town from Idaho.

"I registered to become a donor because my girlfriend asked me to," he shared over dinner. "That was in 1992."

My transplant took place seventeen years later. Hard to believe he even remembered he had registered, much less that the registry was still able to find him. Yet they did, and he held to his word. In all the world's bone marrow registries, only nine people had blood with genetic markers that matched mine, and when called upon, the first few registrants flaked. The fourth call was Matt, and thank God he didn't bag.

Matt continued, "Several times the nurses asked me if I wanted to back out—if I really wanted to go through with it."

He did. He was committed, but it wasn't easy. He had to travel from Moscow, Idaho, home to the University of Idaho, to Spokane, Washington, in order to get to a facility that could perform the stem cell extraction. There he received several shots of a concoction that promotes stem cell growth called Neupogen, which made him feel ill the entire week he stayed in Spokane. Fortunately, the principal at the high school where he taught had given him time off. He had even announced over the intercom to all the students in the school what Matt was off to do.

And Matt stuck with it.

He felt like family even before I met him. In fact, to some degree he indeed *is* family, given that we share the same blood system. It also turns out that Matt and I had both participated in college rugby teams that played each other around the time we were both in school. Who knows? Maybe Matt crushed me under a scrum at some point.

Small world!

As an aside, not all donors need to travel to another city to have their stem cells harvested, a process not dissimilar to giving blood.[36] And not all donors will feel ill from Neupogen (I've never had issues with Neupogen myself).

Registering as a bone marrow donor takes a matter of minutes. In the US, you can register online with the National Marrow Donor Program (NMPD) at bethematch. org. Take a break from this book and do it right now if you haven't already! Sign up, receive a kit in the mail, swab the inside of your cheek, mail it back, and *presto!*— you're registered to possibly one day save a life. One in five hundred registrants do. Perhaps even the life of a child.[37]

---

36   At present, there are three sources of stem cells: peripheral blood stem cells (PBSC) found floating in your blood, actual bone marrow, and umbilical-cord blood. To harvest the first, a donor gives blood though an IV tube, which then flows through a machine not unlike a centrifuge that extracts just the stem cells and then returns the blood to the donor through another IV tube. Alternatively, donors can choose to undergo anesthesia so that doctors can remove liquid marrow from the back of the hip bone with needles (painlessly). Certain hospitals will manage umbilical-cord blood donations at birth.

You can learn more about the mechanics and methods of bone marrow donation, including information about potential side effects, at bethematch. org.

If you are a patient looking for a match but can't find one in any of the world's registries, you and your friends and family can start your own registry drive. You can find guidance online at sites such as marrowdrives.org.

37   Note that the NMDP is tied to the more global Bone Marrow Donors Worldwide (BMDW), a Netherlands-based organization that connects dozens of registries in over fifty countries, a list of which can be found on their site (bmdw.org). If you live outside of the US, go there to find a registry in your country and register (now!).

Interestingly, because of its international connections, over half of the

PART II: HALL OF MIRRORS

---

matches arranged by the NMDP involve either a non-US patient or a non-US donor.

LIFE AS NORMAL: GREATER SEATTLE AREA, SEPTEMBER 2011

"Bye, Daddy," Sofia, now five years old, called sweetly as she pulled the straps of her small, pink Hello Kitty backpack over her tiny shoulders.

"Give me a kiss."

She leaned through the space between the two front seats of my jeep and lightly touched my cheek with her lips.

Luke, at age eight, followed with his standard, "Bye, Daddy—I love you!" something he said without fail anytime he left for anyplace, which I loved and still wonder whether he'll keep up now that he's in middle school.

I pulled out of the drop-off lane at Mercer Island's Lakeridge Elementary and embarked on the strictly enforced thirty-five-mile-per-hour drive north on the island's straight and busy main throughway. At the top of the island, rather than turn right to go to Microsoft, I turned left to head downtown, as I'd left Microsoft a few months before to lead marketing for an exciting start-up founded by the guy who'd first hired me at Microsoft. Such a great group of talented, smart, friendly, and dedicated people—not a bad apple in the bunch.

I have an entrepreneurial bent, so the start-up was a good fit for me. When friends at gatherings asked me how work was going, I'd say, "Great—I feel lucky!" Because I did. I'd had a fun and challenging run at Microsoft, which is full of awesome, smart people, but this was different. As an executive, I was actually in the cockpit helping to fly the airplane.

Once I crossed the I-90 floating bridge to Seattle, I siphoned off onto State Route 99, a raised four-lane freeway that runs along the curved edge of downtown, clean skyscrapers to the right and the expansive and tranquil Puget Sound, a deep aqua blue pocked with green-and-white state-run ferries, to the left, and the jagged Olympic Mountains topped with snow at the horizon.

The start-up occupied the sixth floor of a modest building in Belltown, a hip neighborhood in downtown Seattle. Walking into my office, I spotted a thin, purple disc with a cartoon image of a unicorn on its face on my desk chair. I discovered that each time I pressed the button, the voice of a female unicorn shared a line of advice and wisdom, ranging from "Only use your horn when you have to" to "Think rainbows and magic," which made me laugh out loud. I realized immediately that Patricia, our office manager and head of HR, who also regularly brought in treats she'd baked the night before for the staff to enjoy, had left it there. She knew that, thanks to Luke, who had introduced me to a hilarious cartoon series about unicorns on YouTube, I had a thing for kitschy unicorn stuff. (If you like goofy, off-the-wall humor, check out Charlie the Unicorn on YouTube—you may find it odd or, like me, you might have a chuckle.).

Finally, life proceeded. Life was normal again.

Though not for long.

BUMP

I had never been to a dermatologist before—it was kind of exciting.

I found the office of Dr. Pajat inside a bleached gingerbread cottage sitting daintily on a concrete lawn between a strip mall and an enormous food center in downtown Bellevue. He had decorated the office in angular, modern furniture, giving the space the feel of an art installation.

A stocky Indian man with shiny black hair met me at the front desk, his checkered black-and-violet shirt a sharp match for his dark wool slacks.

"Walter?" he asked without a hint of an accent.

"Yup, that's me."

"Nice to meet you. I'm Dr. Pajat. I'll be with you in just a moment." Flashing a quick smile, he turned and walked back to one of the clinic's two examination rooms. I took a seat in the reception area, which he'd painted entirely in wedding-gown white. Low ceilings made the space feel tight.

I must've hit my head on the Honda...

At least that's what I had been telling myself. The bump was the size of a marble—and felt like one. It didn't hurt. Touch it, ignore it. Touch it, ignore it. I did that for weeks.

That is until, sitting at my desk at the start-up, I happened to run my fingers down the side of my neck and noticed five pea-sized balls of swollen tissue running like a strand of pearls just under the surface of the skin, a discovery that triggered a small jolt of adrenaline.

I called Dr. Austin, who told me to go see a dermatologist she knew in Bellevue. And to see her as well.

His dark slacks fluttering, Dr. Pajat returned to the reception area.

"Follow me," he said, and I trailed him into an examination room in the back where a sleek, black-and-silver metal tool cabinet stood against the far wall.

"Have a seat," he said, pointing to the exam table. "What seems to be the matter?" I told him about the bump on my head.

"I think I hit my head on my car, but it won't go away. Something's off."

"OK, fair enough. Let's take a look." He placed his hands on either side of my head, asked me to lower my chin so he could get a better view of my scalp, and pulled a small penlight from his coat pocket. Squinting, he pointed the light directly at the bump, which he began to palpate with his index finger.

Several seconds passed in silence.

"Walter...this is cancerous."

Looking up, I saw the dismay on Dr. Pajat's face and

knew he was right.

Still, it was 2012 now and this wasn't my first run-in with cancer. I'd been diagnosed with full-blown acute leukemia more than two years earlier and had to endure months of aggressive, bruising treatment. A small cancerous knot on the top of my head felt minor by comparison, more of a curiosity than an alarm.

"I'll take some tissue for biopsy," he said softly, "but I'm certain the mass is malignant. I'm very sorry."

Maybe he doesn't come across cancer that often. He looked so dejected I found myself wanting to place my hand on his shoulder and tell *him* everything would be ok. More likely, of course, was that he didn't realize that cancer wasn't anything new for me.

"I need to call Dr. Austin to discuss next steps," he said. "Can you wait here?"

"Of course."

I waited on the edge of the examination table, more awake than I had been all morning, and let my eyes wander around the room. Not much to see. Just white walls and the shiny tool chest.

When he returned, I noticed Dr. Pajat was breathing hard, like he'd run back or something.

"Dr. Austin agrees we should get the tissue tested. And she wants to see you."

"I'm already on her calendar."

"Great. Here's my card. Call me if you need anything. I'll check in on you tomorrow." Even though he meant well, this struck me as odd. There surely wouldn't be much to talk about. *Well...the bump is still there...*

The moment I stepped out into the chilly February sun I called Angela to tell her what had happened. I detected alarm in her voice as she asked questions. Personally, I didn't feel anxious. Not because I'm particularly intrepid, but because the leukemia, despite regular blood checks, was not part of my life any longer. The transplant itself was barely a memory. I seldom thought about it, and when I did, it felt fuzzy and distant. I was back to indestructibility or, more accurately, I didn't obsess over destructibility. I was free.

So why be thrown off by a little bump?

Angela: I ended up leaving work and driving to Dr. Pajat's office to meet Walt. When I arrived, Dr. Pajat told me unequivocally the bump on his head was cancerous. That there was no doubt.

Walt left to go back to work. I got into my car to try to go back to work, too, but instead called my mother and wept.

The day after my visit with Dr. Pajat, I made my way to see Dr. Austin at her clinic in Issaquah, a burgeoning suburban development covering the low-lying pine-treed hills that foreshadow the towering Cascades east of Seattle.

Placing her fingers on my neck, Dr. Austin said

immediately, "Walt, this could be lymphoma," a statement that got my attention. "Lymphoma is a common secondary cancer for people who've had leukemia," she explained in the concise and direct manner to which I had grown accustomed and found reassuring. "Or it could be leukemia. We won't know until we test it."

The news hit me harder than did Dr. Pajat's. Now, the bump had a name: lymphoma. With the introduction of terminology like "secondary cancer" and "lymphoma," the conversation took on weight.

Secondary cancer? Really? Ugh...I thought we were done with this. Doesn't lymphoma have a high cure rate? I knew very little about it.

"Dr. Pajat will have the results of the tissue test from your head tomorrow," Dr. Austin explained. "Regarding the lymph nodes, you need to get your neck checked out right away."

A few days later, I found myself on an operating table staring up at bright fluorescent lamps in a room crowded with polished steel. Someone had spread a collection of sterile instruments neatly across the top of a rolling cart next to me: scalpels, scissors, tweezers. Three nurses, each in mint-green scrubs and masks, moved about the room in preparation.

"Mr. Harp, I need you to count to three backward," instructed the anesthesiologist now hovering over my face. So I began.

"Three, two..."

I fell unconscious immediately. A surgeon proceeded to cut into the surface of my neck, making a small incision through which he removed one of the swollen lymph nodes. He told me later it was so unstable that it liquefied between his index finger and thumb like a milky gumdrop.

Subsequent testing revealed that leukemia, not lymphoma, had infiltrated the lymph nodes on my neck. I wasn't surprised, given that I had already learned the bump on my scalp was leukemic. Leukemia on my scalp, leukemia in my neck.

"We can take care of this with localized radiation," Dr. Austin told me over the phone. "This isn't a full relapse. It's limited—a minor setback."

With that reassurance, what little tension I felt vanished. I just needed to jump through some hoops to get this fixed. Not a big deal. And there was no lymphoma to deal with. It was the devil I knew, leukemia. And only a tiny bit of it at that.

That evening, I picked up Luke from soccer practice next to the one middle school on Mercer Island. I wasn't thinking about cancer but was instead distracted by the low murmur of NPR on the radio and my enjoyment of my young son, who sat tall in the backseat, his chin rising an inch above the shoulder strap running diagonally across his chest.

"Dad!" came the excited, small voice from behind me.

"What's up, bud?"

"I scored three goals in practice!"

"Nice!"

Luke excelled at soccer, in part because I got him involved at the age of three with a local organization called Lil' Kickers, though the kids, both boys and girls, didn't really play soccer. Class meant kicking a tiny spotted ball at dozens of miniature orange traffic cones strewn across the wooden floor of our local community center's gymnasium, followed by games of Red Light, Green Light and a ragtag contest to see who could hit the coach with the ball.

Luke asked, "Dad, do you know what's the most dangerous shark?"

"No, I don't. What is?"

Animated, Luke replied, "The bull shark. They live in tropical areas and can swim in both saltwater and freshwater!"

"Wow!" I remarked with enough effort to reflect an appropriate level of enthusiasm while still conserving energy since Luke's chattiness, as endearing as it truly was, could be difficult to keep pace with. I sometimes had to tell Luke, albeit as gently as I could, "That's enough questions, sweetheart," else I'd find myself facing fatigue. Other times I'd subtly turn up the volume on *All Things Considered* in the hope that we could ride the rest of the way in silence, which made me feel a little guilty unless we had already gone through a lengthy question-and-answer session. Plus, I knew the number of days in which Luke would be eager to share his many thoughts with me was finite, so I was always appreciative of the Q&A.

"Dad?" Luke called out again.

"Yes?"

"I know how they made it so Mary Poppins could pull so much stuff out of her bag."

"Really? How?"

The floor was still open for questions. I loved it.

The next day, at Dr. Austin's direction, I went to see Dr. Ferguson, a radiologist in his late fifties, with graying hair. He sat a few feet away from me in a sparsely furnished exam room on the first floor of Overlake. Donna, a pleasant nurse practitioner whose hair was also gray, joined us as Dr. Ferguson explained what lay ahead.

"We'll treat the tumor on your scalp with a beam that will cover two inches in diameter," he began. "But your neck is a different story. We'll need to approach that at a thirty-degree angle, which unfortunately means that the beam will catch the side of your face."

Two years ago, in preparation for my stem cell transplant, I had undergone three days of full body radiation while sitting under a gown, basically naked, on a bike seat inside a metal cage in the basement of the University of Washington. I didn't blink at the prospect of radiation spritzing across my cheek.

Dr. Ferguson continued. "Taking into account the radiation you received for the stem cell transplant, the additional radiation will bring the total amount to just over half the maximum we like a patient to have in his lifetime," a statement that caught my attention since I hadn't known there was a maximum.

Yikes...

"Any questions for me?" asked Dr. Ferguson.

"No, sir. Makes sense. You've explained it well."

Another procedure, nothing more. Motion absent emotion.

Dr. Ferguson closed the discussion, saying "We'll take good care of you."

And with that, he left the room. Donna, his assistant, stayed behind. Looking at me through the clear lenses of her large, gold-rimmed glasses, she told me, "After the radiation, you'll have a funny hairdo for a while because of hair loss, but it should grow back after four or five months."

I liked Donna. She was being thoughtful and kind but was, unfortunately, incorrect. The hair never grew back. The asymmetrical pattern left on my head by the radiation remains to this day, part of the reason I now keep my head shaved.

I scheduled all ten radiation sessions for 7 a.m. to be

sure I got to work at a decent time. On the first morning, the receptionist walked me to a waiting room, equivalent in size to a large walk-in closet, in the back of the clinic. An older gentleman and his wife sat next to each other on one of two couches while another man, sporting a full beard, rested on a lounge chair, waiting for his wife. I made myself a cup of coffee from the accordion-sized Starbucks machine perched on a table in the corner and lowered myself onto the open couch. Despite our proximity, no one spoke. But the silence didn't feel awkward. We were all on the same path, and each of us knew that.

Soon, a pretty technician popped around the corner.

"Mr. Harp?" she asked in a slight Russian accent. Rising from my chair, I met her eyes and nodded. She led me to a dark, empty room where a strange white object that resembled a half-ton Stay Puft Marshmallow Man stood frozen, stooped over the flat platform that jutted out from his belly where patients were to lie to receive the radiation that emanated from his round glassy face.

"Do I need to change my clothes?" I asked.

"No, just unbutton the top of your shirt," the nurse replied. I unfastened the top four buttons of my standard-issue, long-sleeve cotton shirt and spread the collar wide, reminding me of Elvis.

"Come lie down," called another of the female technicians, this one standing next to the Marshmallow Man. I walked to where she stood, hoisted myself onto the cot, and lay looking up at the giant's glass face, which gleamed despite the darkness. The day before, I had lain in the same spot while a technician pressed what felt like clay onto my face, carefully massaging it with her fingers to capture every nook. The mold yielded a frozen impression of my visage from which another technician produced a white mask made of fine synthetic webbing that fit my face perfectly.

The radiation required precision, so the technicians placed the mask over my face and locked it to the cot. That way I wouldn't toss about. The technician cut a hole in the top of the mask at the spot where the radiation needed to reach my scalp.

That's a shame. The mask was flawless.

One of the technicians rotated the Marshmallow Man, which in fact was an expensive, sophisticated linear accelerator, until its face overlooked the top of my head. Another technician joined her, and the two of them made a number of micro-adjustments, pausing in between to consult each other until they became satisfied that the high-energy radiation beam would land right where it should. They left the room, and what had been a lighthearted gathering of casual chatter and preparation suddenly turned into silent isolation.

Because I have mild claustrophobia, I started to perform the deep *ujjayi* breathing I'd learned in yoga to keep calm as I lay there in the dark with my head bolted to a platform, unable to move. A few seconds later, I heard a voice come from an overhead speaker.

"Walter, this will last just one minute."

Radiation is silent, so I heard nothing. When the technicians opened the door and returned, I had to take it on faith that something had actually occurred.

"Good job," said one of my technician family as she walked back into the room. I hadn't done anything, really, but spread my collar and remain still on a plastic stretcher in the dark, but I appreciated the warm-fuzzy nonetheless.

"Now let's get you situated so we can tackle your neck."

As Dr. Ferguson had forewarned, when the team aimed the radiation at the swollen lymph nodes in my neck, they couldn't help but catch my face in the process. As a result, I no longer grow hair on the right side of my face, which is nice in that it saves me time shaving. Still, the radiation ended up burning the right side of my neck enough that it broke out in sores and, a few months later, became infected while I was spending a week on vacation with my family in Costa Rica. When we returned, a surgeon had to dig out an abscess—a pocket of pus the size of half a golf ball! It left an open wound that took several weeks to heal and not a small amount of pain to care for, both literally and figuratively. To get all the pus out, the surgeon had to scrape so deep into my neck that he exposed a nerve. Every day when I had to clean and dress the wound, I couldn't avoid hitting the nerve and setting it off like a Taser. And it didn't help that I had to keep stuffing tiny cords like shoelaces into the cavity to soak up moisture—although I found the grossness oddly fascinating, the way a boy does when squishing bugs.

The sessions at Overlake Radiology Oncology passed quickly, thankfully. Each morning was a simple rinse and repeat: spread my collar, lie on the table, brave the mask, get radiated, grab free coffee from the Starbucks machine, go to work. Unfortunately, two months after the last session, I found myself back at the clinic after discovering a hard lump in my testes while in the shower, an unmistakable and alarming sensation. Rather than procrastinate, my usual modus operandi, I called Dr. Austin right away. I was still dripping water with a towel around my waist when we scheduled an appointment for the next day.

"There's definitely a bump there," said Dr. Austin in a soft but steady voice after she finished the exam, her once-smiling face now slack and serious. She didn't sound alarmed, which kept me at ease. Besides, as I shared earlier, by this time I was relatively numb to news of more cancer.

The next day I showed up for a CT scan at the imaging clinic located down the hall from Dr. Austin's clinic at Swedish Hospital. There I lay on a plastic sled that slid me head-first in and out of the center of an enormous powdered donut lined with highly sensitive x-ray machines. The scan produced a series of images of my groin that would enable Dr. Austin to see what was transpiring inside my scrotum.

The process took all of twenty minutes. Just another procedure I forgot about thirty seconds after the fact.

When Dr. Austin called the next morning, she told me

that the scans revealed not one lump, but a number of them, along with a collection of lesions. My mind tried to form a picture of what that must look like on film.

I had read that leukemic cells will hide in the testicles, so the news made perfect sense. It's as if Dr. Austin was telling me that round pegs go in round holes and square pegs in square ones.

Of course.

We were simply chasing a cadre of blasts from hideout to hideout. First, they were in a bump on my scalp, next in the nodes on my neck, and now in my testes. Their path was almost predictable. Angela felt the same way.

"Of course, the hold-out blasts are entrenched in a known sanctuary," she said. "We'll smoke 'em out."

Still, when I saw Dr. Ferguson at Overlake Radiation, he looked grim.

"I'm sorry to see you back," he said soberly. "But we'll take care of you. It'll be like last time. Ten sessions and you'll be done."

His assistant, Donna, handed me a tube of salving cream. "In case you develop a rash," she said.

Each morning over the next ten days, I found myself back on the table in the dark room looking up at the Marshmallow Man, only this time with my pants down. Yes, I was a relatively mature grown man, but it was hard not to feel a tad self-conscious while two women shifted both the linear accelerator and my scrotum back and forth to line the two up!

As with the series of radiation to my head and neck, the mornings passed quickly, and once again the cancer went into remission. With nary a leukemic blast to be found, leukemia again faded back into the background. Sure, it remained floating over my shoulder and could tap it on any given day, but it wasn't in the front of my mind.

At least for a couple of months, it wasn't.

"The tests of your CSF came back positive," Dr. Austin explained.

Cerebrospinal fluid (CSF) is the clear liquid that fills the sac encasing and protecting the spinal nerves. The brain floats in it. Leukemia is a blood disease, and blood doesn't mix with the CSF because the circulatory system and spinal sac are separate—kept apart by a selectively permeable membrane that forms what's known as the blood–brain barrier. Still, tenacious leukemic blasts will sometimes cross the chasm and make their way into the CSF.

When medical researchers first came to understand the nature of leukemia in the blood and began treating patients with chemo, some who achieved remission would return weeks later suffering from seizures, only to die soon thereafter. The baffled scientists later learned that while they had gotten rid of all the blasts in the blood, other blasts had infiltrated the CSF, where they multiplied and formed a lethal force.

It was one thing for me to have blasts show up in my scalp or lymph nodes or testes. Blasts in my cerebrospinal fluid, though? That was a whole new game. And one I didn't like. I knew that the presence of blasts in the CSF worsened the odds of survival, which weren't great to begin with. Dr. Austin's news didn't send me to the canvas, but it certainly landed a punch.

As you may recall, in order to get chemo into the spinal fluid, doctors have to stick a needle between the patient's lower vertebrae and puncture the spinal sac, which when you are awake is not the most comfortable procedure on the planet. Fortunately, innovation has brought about the ability to embed a small, synthetic funnel under the patient's scalp that feeds into the CSF reservoir in the brain. Once the funnel, called an Ommaya reservoir, is in place, a physician can inject chemo into the CSF by puncturing the skin covering the reservoir with a needle, a procedure that's relatively painless. No more digging around with needles in the spine.

To proceed with the Ommaya, Dr. Austin sent me to see a neurosurgeon, who turned out to be tall and attractive with long, tanned legs.

Supermodel plus brain surgeon...

"The surgery is outpatient," explained Dr. Carrilon. "I'm simply going to place the reservoir under your scalp. You'll be under full anesthesia and done before you know it."

"I need this like I need a hole in the head."

"Ha! I actually haven't heard that one before."

A few days later, I reported to Swedish Hospital's surgery unit, where the operation proceeded apace. Angela took me home the same day and I was told not to remove the large bandage they had placed over my scalp. When it came time to peel it back, I found that a semicircle of half-inch staples now bordered the exact spot where Donna at Dr. Ferguson's office had told me my hair would grow back post-radiation. Not only was the spot still bald and discolored; now little metal crossbars give it a decorative outline. A small lump rose in the middle of the barren stretch, and the Ommaya protruded from under the skin. Altogether, the top of my head now sported a slightly discolored, asymmetrical moonscape with a small mountain jutting up from the ground.

Any remaining shred of vanity I still held onto vanished.

I wore a baseball cap on my first day back to the start-up so as not to freak out coworkers with the sight of my Frankenstein head, but I ended up having to remove the hat every ten minutes or so to give the muscles of my scalp a break. Because my head is so large, all ball caps, regardless of size, grow uncomfortable after a short time. Halfway through the day, I decided enough was enough and ditched the hat. Oddly, no one blinked.

After work, walking along the dark streets of downtown Seattle, I fancied that perhaps the staples and scars on my head made me look intimidating to the imaginary thugs who might otherwise want to mess with me. A stranger at Jack in the Box asked me if I'd been in the service. Luke, at this point eight years old called them out proudly to teammates at one of his Little League games. When walking with me, Sofia, now five, exclaimed to almost everyone we met, "My Dad had cancer!" as she pointed to the staples.

Angela: Despite the leukemia's relentless recurrence—albeit locally, fortunately, and not yet in Walt's bone marrow—we managed to function relatively normally. In fact, a week after Walt got the Ommaya, we took a family trip to Costa Rica, which was glorious. Luke blissfully chased geckos. Sofia rode a horse and drove an ATV while sitting in Walt's lap. I got to capture the family in photos that to this date I'm most proud of.

I attribute the vacation and relative calm to Walt's sheer ability to endure procedure after procedure. No whining, no perseverating—just doing what had to be done.

Oddly, it was a period without fear. I think Walt was compartmentalizing what had yet to become a major threat. And as long as he could lead a normal life—family, work, exercise, play—and as long as he felt healthy and energetic—which he did the entire time—he was fine.

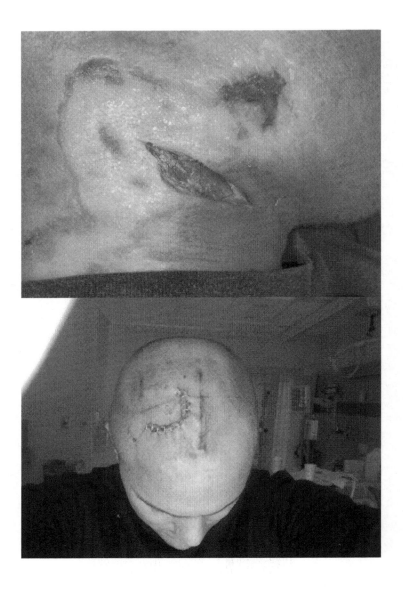

Above The infected cavity where an abscess was removed (early spring 2012). I hated cleaning that thing.

Below: X marks the spot where the Ommaya reservoir now lives (late spring 2012). The semicircle of staples is pretty striking.

NOTHING TO WORRY ABOUT

Tall pine trees stood dark in the distance against the luminescent turquoise sky behind the modern glass and brick building that is Swedish Hospital, Issaquah. Seattle summer was on its way, scintillating and pristine.

Inside the building, I sat on a blue chair across from Dr. Austin as she finished updating my med list in the hospital's digital record system.

"Here's where we're at," she began. "I still don't think we should move to full chemo."

That's good...

"It's not like you've had a systemic relapse. It's been local. Where we've seen the leukemia show up, we've hit it. There are no blasts in your blood or marrow, so there's nothing for chemo to attack. Chemo at this point would simply be pre-emptive, and there's no research to indicate that chemo can be used prophylactically. My belief is that if a full-blown relapse is going to come, it will come. And we'll deal with it then. Plus, there's a quality of life issue I think we need to consider. There's no need to put you in a hospital bed."

As I listened to her calming, studied logic, I felt the burn from the morning's caffeine clear from my eyes and the tension in the muscles of my back release. The blasts in my scalp, the lymph nodes in my neck, the testes, the CSF— these were all cases of leukemic rebels making stubborn last stands. My blood was clear, and I was free to go.

CHICKEN HOT DOG

Dressed in dark tights spotted with fluorescent pug faces and the pink T-shirt I had bought her on a business trip to Madrid, Sofia, five years old, reclined next to me on the red microfiber sectional Angela and I had bought back when we lived in New York—furniture we chose because microfiber is spill resistant and our children were spill-prone.

"Knock, knock," Sofia said suddenly.

"Who's there?" I asked.

"Chicken…"

"Chicken who?"

"Chicken hot dog!" she exclaimed.

My daughter's humor isn't linear. She is the master of, well, the unexpected. Random associations. She finds the obvious boring, and I, too, appreciate quirkiness.

"What'd you do today?" I asked, though I already knew she'd spent the day at school and that the chances of Sofia giving a meaningful response to such a mundane question were nil. I wasn't surprised when she said nothing.

"What'd you do?" I asked again, repeating my error and thus failing at conversation. Sofia offered up a single word without making the effort to look up from her book.

"Stuff," she said succinctly. Sofia wasn't being rude. This was Sofia being wry while also staying true to her natural inclination not to engage in banality. I should've known better.

"Oh yeah? Guess what I did at work today?" I asked with enough enthusiasm to get her to look up.

"What?" she asked.

I turned away and held silent for several seconds.

"Stuff," I answered nonchalantly.

Sofia made a conscious effort to keep her face from registering a reaction, yet failed to prevent a slight upturn in the sides of her mouth, betraying her appreciation for the repartee.

I love my daughter immensely and would do anything for her. She is sweet, thoughtful, and kind. But she's also tough in certain regards, something I'm very proud of. And I'll admit my little girl is also a bit stubborn. Angela and I both know there are things Sofia simply won't agree to, no matter what we do, and when she digs her heels in, it's like she's rooted them in titanium. Many a painful battle has taught me to be more patient with her, to let certain conflicts unwind in due course rather than attempt to force a resolution.

This wasn't always the case, though. One time, when Sofia was three years old and we were all riding in a car together after disembarking from a Washington State Ferry that had returned us to Anacortes from Orcas Island, she wouldn't stop kicking the back of my seat—no matter how many times I asked. I ended up pulling the car over to the side of the road, opening the passenger door on the side where she was sitting, and removing her tennis shoes. Her response? Sofia screamed relentlessly for miles. Screamed not in fright but in raw, unmitigated anger, until finally I capitulated, pulled over to the shoulder once again, and put her shoes back on.

It took several such incidents over the span of Sofia's early years before I finally realized there would simply be moments when Sofia's stubbornness would outlast mine and I'd do best by staying patient.

Back on the couch, while Sofia continued reading, I glanced down at my iPhone and was reminded that most of the apps on it were Sofia's. It made me wonder what someone would think were they to find my phone on a table somewhere—if I left it in the conference room at work, for example. Sure, I had a few apps for grown-ups—mail, calendar, and maps—but most were things like Princess Party, Fashion Runway, and Bunny Adventure.

Eventually bored with my phone, I faked a menacing expression, turned to face Sofia, and held up a fist in jest. She looked up from her book, turned to face me as well, and lifted *two* fists in response. I matched her by adding my other fist to the mix. Now we were tied: two fists to two. Sofia stood up, raised her leg to feign a kicking stance, and transformed one of her fists into a gun and the other into a chainsaw and thereby won what was an oft-repeated derivation of tic-tac-toe that some may find odd, or perhaps a bit graphic, but I found highly entertaining.

It always ended in my having to cower in surrender once Sofia established clear dominance.

Later that night, long after the game of brinkmanship and minutes after I had turned off the lights and closed my eyes in the master bedroom, I heard Sofia open the door and in her small voice say, "I want to snuggle." Sofia's not a big snuggler, at least not with me (maybe a little bit with her mom), so the proclamation took me by surprise.

"OK. Hop into bed."

As Sofia nestled against my shoulder, I couldn't have felt happier. Angela doesn't really like the kids sleeping in our bed. I, on the other hand, love it, particularly since I know that one day soon the kids will stop wanting to do that.

"Mommy will be angry if I stay too long," Sofia said into my shoulder.

"OK. No problem. Leave whenever you want."

Of course, we both promptly fell asleep.

EN ROUTE TO CURE

The next morning, I found myself back at the SCCA for what they call "long-term follow-up," my sixth check-in to date. Walking worry-free through the glass front doors, I wasn't thinking about the Ommaya in my scalp or the localized radiation I had gone through for my neck and testes months earlier. I was clear and free of leukemia. All the localized relapses were now memories.

The literature on leukemia states that once someone has remained in remission for five years, that person is considered cured.[38] Dr. Austin told me that for all practical purposes a patient is cured after *three* years, given that the chances of relapse beyond that milestone are negligible. I had suffered local relapses, but I didn't think of myself as having truly relapsed. The leukemia hadn't reappeared in my blood; it had just shown up here and there in an attempted last stand. As far as I was concerned, I was two and a half years out from transplant and, having not fully relapsed, six months away from being considered cured.

The SCCA's Long-Term Follow-Up Unit (LTFU) resides on the building's sixth floor. Floor-to-ceiling windows form a concave arc offering a breathtaking, panoramic view of downtown Seattle's Lake Union. Fronting the glass is a line of minimalist reclining chairs, prime real estate in a waiting area that is usually at full occupancy. Every now and then, on my luckiest days, I would happen upon an open spot.

The sixth-floor reception space includes a designated play area for children marked by a Nintendo and large monitor ensconced in a refrigerator-sized shelf made of particleboard. I have never seen a child actually using the Nintendo. In fact, I haven't seen many children at the SCCA, period. When I *have* seen them, it's usually the adult

---

38   I recall feeling slightly envious of Lance Armstrong in that testicular cancer
      is cured after one year in remission, a fact I learned from his book It's Not
      About the Bike: My Journey Back to Life. Love him or hate him for the whole
      doping scandal thing, the book tells a great story of survival and comeback.
      It's well worth the read.

they're with who's getting care, although when I see the small white feeding tube in a baby's nose or the telltale hat covering a small child's hairless head, I recognize it is the child who is ill.

The parents must be beside themselves.

Every time I went to the SCCA for follow-up, the receptionist on the sixth floor would hand me a meticulously detailed itinerary. It might list appointments that crossed all disciplines, from dental to pulmonary to cardiac to you-name-it. But all in one building, which made the visits incredibly efficient. On this day, though, I was to spend but an afternoon. A simple check-in. A few tests. That's all.

Spacious and bright, the SCCA's respiratory exam room held little furniture save for a computer desk, while next to it sat a squat glass booth with a stool inside. A floor-to-ceiling picture of a sunny beach, no doubt intended to keep patients cheery, decorated one of the walls.

"Welcome, welcome—have a seat!" exclaimed the technician perched at the desk. The hefty volume of her voice took me off guard. "I'm Stephanie!"

Small, stout, and lovely, with graying hair, her energy burst through the buttons of her lab coat. I wondered how someone could maintain such enthusiasm when doing the same thing day in and day out. I liked her immediately.

At Stephanie's direction, I slid inside the Plexiglas phone booth and sat facing forward on the stool. It was a good thing the glass created a sense of openness because I found the booth very tight.

"Place your mouth around the tube," Stephanie instructed.

I wrapped my lips around the black rubber mouthpiece hanging directly in front of my face as if it were the bottom of a snorkel, which in this case ran out of the top of the booth and into the cavity of some respiratory-gauging instrument.

"When I tell you to, I want you to breathe in as much air as you can," Stephanie continued. "*Slowly*, ok? And when I say 'blow it out,' you're to exhale *as hard and as fast as you can*. I want the oxygen out of there—*fast*! Keep blowing until it's totally and completely gone. Got it?"

"Yebb," I replied, trying to keep an airtight seal on the mouthpiece.

"Ready?"

"Yegg."

"On the count of three, breathe in. One...two...three! BREATHE IN!" she shouted.

"HOOOOOO!"

"KEEP BREATHING! BREATHE MORE!"

"WHUUUUUUUU!"

"ONE MORE SIP!"

"EEEEEEEE!"

"NOW BLOW IT OUT!"

"HOOOOOOOOOOOooooo..."

"BLOW! BLOW! BLOW!"

"Wheeeeeeee..."

"BLOW SOME MORE."

"Eeeeeeeee..."

"Nice job, Walter. Let's see how you did."

Stephanie stared at the computer monitor, and then started typing.

"How'd I do?" I asked after what felt like a long silence.

"Well, we need to do this at least two more times to make sure we've got it. And then we have a bunch more tests to run through."

I realized I was in for a marathon.

Gird yourself.

"Ready?" she asked.

My lungs exhausted and my head dizzy, I thanked Stephanie after we'd finished and took an elevator up two floors to see one of the staff dentists, who wrote me a prescription for toothpaste that, probably to my detriment, I later placed in a drawer in the bathroom at home and never used. I met with a physical therapist, who asked me to take a stamina test by speed-walking up and down a hallway, leaving me certain I was going to crash into someone entering from one of the adjoining offices.

Then came the most important appointment of the day: the clinic. I was to first meet with a nurse for a physical exam, and then with the Long-Term Follow-Up Unit's most senior nurse for an additional examination, and *then* with the LTFU's attending physician. I made my way to one of the nearly thirty examination rooms on the sixth floor, each barely large enough to fit a sink, countertop, and exam bed, along with three adults max. Any more people would turn the room into a clown car.

A clear testament to their dedication and the institution's integrity, all the nurses I met at the SCCA had worked there for a decade, if not two or more. Knowledgeable and kind, they are among the best of the best. Ellen was no exception.

"Hi, Walter. I'm Ellen. I'm going to be your nurse today," announced a short woman wearing her blonde hair in a bun. "Should I call you Walt or Walter?"

"Either is fine," I said, smiling. "'Hey, you.' Whatever."

"OK, then. I need you to put on that gown and have a seat. I'll step out to give you some privacy. Just open the door when you're ready."

I dutifully removed all my clothes, save my boxers, and, after fumbling with the snaps for what felt like forever, pulled the gown over my head and opened the door. As happened at all LTFU clinic sessions, Ellen first checked my blood pressure and temperature, then walked through the med list the SCCA had recorded to make sure their database reflected what I was actually taking. Next, she began a series of tests to assess my flexibility. She wanted to determine whether the donor's blood cells had attacked tissue in my joints.

"Put your hands in front of your chest and place your palms together," Ellen instructed.

I placed my hands in prayer and pulled them down to my sternum. Both hands flexed backward at the wrists. Ellen took a photo.

"Good, your wrists are fine. Now turn around and place your right hand behind the nape of your neck and bring your left hand behind your back. See if you can get one hand to touch the other."

I did my best to do as she asked, but couldn't manage to get my fingers to touch. I'm not the most flexible guy on the planet and wouldn't have been able to touch my fingers in that fashion *before* the transplant, so my failure to do so didn't raise a red flag.

Ellen snapped another photo with her camera.

"OK, just a few more."

Before long, Ellen and I were joined by Julie, the LTFU's senior nurse. Julie and I had become friends from previous visits to the SCCA. Vibrant and intelligent, she knew (and knows) as much about transplant care as anyone.

"How are you feeling?" she asked.

"Great," I replied from my perch on the exam table. "You still running marathons?"

"I don't know that I'd call it running, but I manage to make it to the finish line." She laughed.

"I'm envious!"

Julie and I continued to chat for a few minutes before getting down to the task at hand.

"Do me a favor and take off your gown so I can look at your skin," Ellen requested politely. She wanted to see whether GVHD (graft-versus-host disease) had caused any inflammation. I removed the gown and Julie ran her hand across my back and arms, looking for anything that would suggest a rash.

"You eating ok?"

"Yes—plenty," I said, squeezing a healthy fold of stomach skin, which made Julie laugh.

"Now place your palms together in front of you like this." Ellen had already asked me to do the same, but I did as I was told, thinking perhaps it was protocol to double-check certain tests.

We completed several more exercises, and then an older woman wearing round glasses with thick black rims walked in. Short in stature but heavy on presence, she filled the room before speaking a word.

"I'm Nancy Getzen," she said with a smile and what I took for a German accent. I detected a sharp mind spinning at high speed behind those glasses.

Dr. Getzen walked up to me and took hold of my hand.

She looked up at me and sweetly asked, "Do you have children?"

That's an odd question. And why is there concern in her voice?

"Yes," I replied, thinking the answer should be clearly stated in my SCCA records. "A daughter age five and a son age eight." I stared at her, puzzled.

Dr. Getzen crinkled her forehead in an expression of sympathy.

"Aw," she murmured. "We need to keep you around for them."

What did she say? "Keep me around?" What? Where am I going?

"They need their dad…"

Umm, yes they do. Why are you speaking to me like I'm in danger?

"You need chemo, radiation, and a second transplant."

What?

DISBELIEF

I heard the words but immediately rejected them as unreal. It was as if I had heard a zebra open its mouth and speak.

I was disoriented. *What is she talking about? Hasn't she*

spoken with Dr. Austin?

The room felt hot and crowded and I grew disoriented. The floor began to list like an injured submarine. I stared blankly at Dr. Getzen, not sure how to process the irrationality of what she was saying. She looked back at me gracefully. Expectantly. As if waiting to receive my reaction—which was one of shock and anger.

"How do you feel about what I'm telling you?" she asked with calm intensity.

I looked down at my feet to give the emotion a chance to dissipate while the rapidly firing synapses in my head tried to form coherent thoughts.

"Well...this isn't exactly what I expected," I said, looking at her directly once again, irritated and confused.

"Of course," she said gently.

"I don't understand. I haven't relapsed. What are you talking about?"

"Yes, Walter, you have relapsed. I'm sorry, but you have. And you need to think about next steps."

"But it's only been local."

"It's local only for *now*. It won't stay that way."

I lowered my head again to process what I was hearing. *She's wrong. There's no way.*

"There's research happening," Dr. Getzen went on. "You never know what new treatments might arise, and the longer we keep you around, the more options there will be."

Two plus two does not equal five. What planet is this?

The four of us stood in silence. Julie and Ellen both looked at me sympathetically while I grappled with the lunacy. The processor in my head wouldn't accept the input from the keyboard. I couldn't fathom another transplant.

Second transplants don't work. People just relapse again and die.[39]

Dr. Getzen broke the silence. "I'm going to call Dr. Austin to discuss next steps," she said, cupping her hands around mine, holding them for several seconds while searching my face.

In the SCCA's dark-gray concrete parking lot located several floors beneath the earth, I slid into my jeep and started the engine. Lost in thought and therefore unaware of what I was doing, I drove up the ramp on autopilot, paid the toll taker in the booth, and rolled out onto the wet, black asphalt in front of the building. Night had already fallen, so I turned on the headlights and embarked on the familiar route home. I didn't get far, though. After a few blocks, I pulled into an alley, put the automatic transmission in park, and called my mother.

It was six in the evening in Seattle, so it was nine o'clock in Virginia, where she lived. I knew she'd be up. The phone

---

39   I wasn't, in fact, correct. People can be cured by second transplants, though the odds are low.

rang as the engine churned.

"Mom, the leukemia is back," I said plainly when my mother answered the phone. "I need another transplant. Chemo. The whole thing."

"I'm sorry," she said gingerly. Her reaction didn't come close to matching the vexation I felt, so I tried again.

"Mom—seriously. I'm going to have to go back to the hospital. And this time I'm not going to survive. People don't survive second transplants."

"Aww, sweetie...I'm so sorry."

This was going to be full-on chemo and a second transplant—and I was going to die. Yet she was reacting as if I'd simply stubbed my toe or lost my backpack at school.

My mother is a Samaritan by all measures. Kind, loving, and generous to a fault. But, she's not emotive. Not a big hugger, snuggler, or kisser, nor one for tearful hellos or goodbyes. Yes, a worrier—big time—but not warm and fuzzy. If I'd wanted emotional validation, I should have called Angela.

Holding the phone to my ear, I put the jeep in reverse and backed into the alley, only to feel a distinct bump against my back fender.

Oh crap!

Looking in the rearview mirror, I saw the back of a red Honda Accord with its brake lights on. I'd bumped it, albeit at barely a crawl.

"Mom—hold on." I pulled forward, put the phone in the cup holder, stepped out of the jeep, and walked around it. The two bumpers were three feet apart. There was no damage. Zilch. I had been rolling so slowly I would have caused more damage kicking the Honda's bumper with my bare foot.

The woman driving the Accord exited her car and marched toward me, holding her hands in tense fists at her sides. I could see her grimace. She was seething.

"You're not supposed to be talking on the phone," she spit, her lips tight with rage.

"I'm sorry," I replied, feeling the need to diffuse the tension while at the same time irritated at what was an overreaction. *I feel bad for backing into you, but really— you're livid?*

The woman bent down and ran her hand across the Accord's bumper, then stood and stared at me with every muscle in her face clenched.

"You shouldn't be talking on the phone while driving!" she scolded again.

I was talking on the phone. She has a point. "Sorry," I repeated, this time a little sheepishly. She turned and marched back to her car.

Driving out of the alley seconds later, I had an epiphany and stepped on the brakes. I looked again in the rearview mirror and confirmed what I had realized: the woman had been driving in the wrong lane! She was exiting the two-lane alley from the *left* lane, the lane you're supposed to use to *enter* the alley. Unless you are driving in England, Australia, or Hong Kong, that is. No wonder I had bumped into her.

Grrr.

Before heading home, I stopped at a cozy bar on the corner of Eastlake and Republican, a few blocks from the SCCA. I'm not sure I wanted a drink as much as I wanted a break from reality. A chance to breathe. I walked in and sat at one of the small wooden tables, where I texted a friend from work to see if he wanted to join me. It was just a vanilla invite—"Hey, wanna grab a beer?"—with no mention of cancer. Unfortunately, he was already on his bike heading home, far from the bar, so I sat there in the hazy room sipping a pint, thinking of nothing in particular, taking in the ambiance. When I finished the beer and stepped out of the bar, I looked out onto the buildings of downtown Seattle freckled with yellow windows and laced in sooty fog. A light sprinkle freshened my face.

It was beautiful.

As usual, the cul-de-sac where my family and I lived was dark. No light shone anywhere save for the muted glow of curtained windows. In fact, of all the houses in the cul-de-sac, it was mine that produced the most light, since we never closed the shades on the windows overlooking the street.

I shut the car door and walked into the house, glad to be home with the ones I loved in a place that I loved. Angela wasn't back yet. There were only Angela's parents, Eric and Alice, and my life's greatest passions, Luke and Sofia. Even though they lived in a retirement community in Walnut Creek, California, Eric and Alice also owned a modest condo in Bellevue, a stone's throw from Mercer Island. It wasn't unusual at all to see them on a weeknight, particularly since Alice made us dinner most nights. She was (and is) a master of tasty Chinese fare.

I put on my best face.

"Hi, guys!"

"Hi, Walt!" welcomed Eric.

"What's for dinner?" I asked. "Smells good!"

"Sea bass," Alice answered from the kitchen, humorously donning an exaggerated, fanciful look on her face. "It was on special."

I love sea bass, especially the way Alice cooks it with soy sauce. It's not cheap, though. I dropped my bag on the couch and sat in one of the six orange enamel chairs that circumscribed the small brown table outside the kitchen.

"Dinner's ready!" Alice announced.

Luke and Sofia had already eaten, so Alice, Eric, and I sat together. Alice placed six different dishes on the table, including the sea bass, seasoned tofu, and broccoli roasted in oil and garlic. Eric opened a bottle of red wine.

Angela used to joke that I would never volunteer news, I'd always keep it to myself, which at the time was pretty accurate. That night, though, I shared with Alice and Eric what Dr. Getzen had told me. Both sat with quiet intensity as I relayed the facts. As I finished, we heard the front door open and the sound of shuffling feet followed by a warm "Hello!" Something you could always count on from Angela even if she felt worn out after the day.

"Hey—I need to tell you something." I stood up from the table and walked across the room to meet her at the top of the stairs.

Angela looked at me and her smile faded. "What is it?"

I called Dr. Austin first thing the next morning.

"Dr. Getzen and I talked last night," she began. "I respect her point of view but don't agree with it. As I've said all along, your relapse is not systemic. It would be pre-emptive to undergo a heavy chemo regimen at this point, much less a second transplant. Again, there's no data to support the idea of using chemo prophylactically. There's nothing in your blood to kill and using chemo now won't prevent the leukemia from coming back later."

I immediately felt relieved.

"So you think Dr. Getzen was wrong...?"

"You're a unique case, Walt. We should approach your treatment step by step, not jump ahead."

Thank God. I knew it! I had been given a reprieve.

BEER

The sun burned down hot where Phil and I sat at a small, burnished metal table outside the Virginian, a historic bar in the Seattle neighborhood of Belltown. We were relaxing in front of two pints, each of us wearing sunglasses to filter the glare. Over two months had passed since I saw Dr. Getzen at the SCCA, and the alarm had long since settled (basically it settled the moment Dr. Austin told me I didn't need a second transplant). Leukemia was no longer holding a gun to my face. It was back to playing the role of a gentle (though frequent) reminder that everything is fragile and temporary.

A kind and generous friend and father of two, Phil had worked with me at Microsoft at one point and was now at his own start-up. The two of us caught up on work and family, sprinkling the conversation with off-color remarks that made us both laugh. As always, it was great to see him.

A young, blonde waitress in a white T-shirt with rolled-up sleeves approached the table, carrying the leather-bound pad she used for taking orders.

"Would you like a second round?"

I glanced at Phil, who gave a subtle nod.

"Yes, that'd be great," I told the server, "although I think I'll try the IPA."

"And any food for you guys?"

Again I looked at Phil and again we had the same answer.

"Nah, I think we're fine. Just the drinks." The waitress turned away.

Looking up at the sun, I wondered why it didn't feel hotter outside than it did.

It's the breeze that's keeping things cool.

My phone rang. The name on the screen read "Dr. Austin." I had been dropping by her clinic weekly for the last couple of months for blood monitoring. Dr. Austin usually didn't call me herself, so I knew that even though the caller ID said it was her, it could easily be someone else from her office. Still, a small band of butterflies fluttered in my stomach.

"I need to answer this," I told Phil as I pressed the green button on the screen to accept the call.

"Hi, Walt."

The instant I heard Dr. Austin's voice, I knew something was wrong. She always spoke in a soft tone when she had bad news. In fact, it was really *only* when there was bad news that she called; otherwise, it was a voicemail from Marion, one of the nurses.

"The kidney enzymes in your blood are abnormally high," Dr. Austin began. "They're very high."

My stomach tightened.

"I need you to come in for a CT scan tomorrow at nine."

It was just the kidneys. Another local incursion. Still, I was shaken.

"What's up?" Phil asked after I'd hung up.

There was no sense in holding back. Phil was a friend. He knew my history.

"That was my oncologist. She thinks the leukemia could be in my kidneys."

"Fuck. That totally sucks. Is there anything I can do?"

"No. I'm good. Let's finish our beers."

No real alarm. Just some bad news I had to compartmentalize so I could move on.

A couple of days later the results of the CT scan showed my kidneys had swollen to twice their normal size—and they were saturated with leukemic blasts.

"It's time, Walt," said Dr. Austin, her intense blue eyes focused on mine. "I need to admit you for chemo."

Luckily, unlike Dr. Getzen, she didn't say the word "transplant." That would have been devastating. What I *did* hear Dr. Austin say was that the leukemia was in my kidneys, which I interpreted to mean *just* in my kidneys; that the leukemia hadn't infiltrated my bloodstream. Maybe Dr. Austin said something and I blocked it out, but in my mind this was a kidney issue, not a relapse. No one had pressed the panic button.

It wasn't until months later during a side conversation with Dr. Austin that I came to learn that by the time I had come in for the CT scan, blasts already accounted for 30 percent of my white blood cells. It wasn't just a kidney thing. It was a full relapse.

Angela, the kids, and I were scheduled to spend the next few days with good friends of ours at a lake community in eastern Washington, a fun and relaxing vacation spot with a water park, wineries, local barbeques, beaches, swimming pools, water skiing, jet skiing, biking, all surrounded by gorgeous red and orange glacier-carved foothills.

"Can it wait until next week?" I asked Dr. Austin. "We're supposed to go on vacation tomorrow."

She paused. "If we don't hurry up, your kidneys are going to fail," she said sternly.

"Next Wednesday?"

She paused again. "OK."

Angela: The reason Dr. Austin let us go to Chelan? She figured it was a last hoorah. The end was coming. Let us have a bit of fun with our family before Walt dies.

I felt fine for the most part in Chelan. Other than going to bed earlier than usual, I stayed active and involved. I marked the summer, as I always do, by jumping into a freshwater lake. The ocean doesn't count. It has to be a lake. At least that's what I consider traditional given that I grew up in the land-locked Midwest. There's really nothing quite as invigorating as diving into twenty feet of cold, fresh lake water.

I don't know if it's crowded at other times of the year, but Chelan was placid. It felt as if we had the entire place to ourselves, and Angela and I enjoyed every minute, particularly the simple pleasure of watching Luke and Sofia laugh and frolic outdoors with friends.

We ended up renting a jet ski, a trip highlight, marking the second time I had ever been on one in my life. I'm not a rabid jet skier by any stretch. To be honest, I find them a little boring. Sure, they get the adrenaline pumping at first, but after half an hour, I'm usually ready to go home and read a book. This time, though, I had one of the best experiences I've ever had on the water, a thrill I'll never forget: I took Luke and Sofia with me and, one by one, let them sit in front of me and steer. Luke, at nine years old, burned through the water like Superman flying over Metropolis, leaving a tall white spray of water behind him. It was fun! And I felt proud at how quickly he mastered the skill.

Then came Sofia's turn. At only six years old, she opened up the throttle like a pro and shot even faster across the lake than her brother had! I kept my hands on the steering as a safety measure while laughing uncontrollably as she rocketed us forward. Such a pistol.

I didn't fret about the forthcoming chemo while we were in Chelan, but in the back of my mind I did feel like I was counting down the hours to the date of surrender to a federal minimum-security prison. The feeling wasn't one of auspiciousness.

The day after we returned to Seattle, I went to hot yoga at the studio I had been going to regularly.

This is going to be the last class you'll have in a while, so appreciate it.

BACK ON THE SLAB

As it had in the past, leukemia was about to rip me out of my life and take me away from everything: playing with my children, exercising, work—all the things I enjoy. I was standing at the entryway to the parallel universe that is cancer, one that surrounds us, but one we only truly notice—and come to know—when we or someone we love falls through the portal to the other side.

Wednesday came and I reported to the cancer ward on the fourth floor at Overlake Hospital in Bellevue. A prim nurse led me to a room where a gown awaited me on the bed. The overcast sky through the window made the gray interior that much darker as I climbed onto the bed and surrendered. Angela sat quietly next to me.

Sure, I was "fighting" the disease. The concept of fighting felt good. It personified the cancer. Made it something I could swing at, something I could attack.

In reality, though, I couldn't outsmart the leukemia, couldn't out-exercise it, out-work it, out-punch it, out-anything it. As difficult as the truth was to accept—and it *was* very difficult to accept—I had no control over my fate. The leukemia would simply run its course. Chemistry and biology would determine the outcome.[40]

As I embarked on the week of chemo, Angela had to manage the house, the kids, and her job while also finding time to spend with me, which she did every day without fail. All while being afraid, if not terrified. She was the one who would be left behind if I died, left to console the kids, left to keep the family afloat financially and keep the children in the schools and community they were accustomed to. She would be the one left alone in the house to pack memories in boxes. I had it easy by comparison.

Nurses shuttled in and out of the drab room without a sound. I recognized one of them from my very first stay at Overlake, a wry young man named Graham. It was nice to see a familiar face.

Another nurse ferried in a large, clear plastic bag of hydration fluid and hung it from my IV pole. She smiled and left the room.

And that's when my screen went black. For whatever reason, I don't remember anything from that week at

---

40   Of course, many believe differently—that patients can influence outcomes through things like prayer, attitude, and alternative medicine. Which is completely legitimate. I'm not making a broad argument here, just explaining my view at the time.

Overlake. It just disappeared.

A few days after discharge from my lost week at Overlake, I walked into Dr. Austin's clinic at Swedish with what felt like the flu. Body aches, fever, light-headedness. Marion, one of the nurses, looked at me and blanched. I looked like a ghoul. She knew right away that something was very wrong.

A second nurse appeared and led me to a small room in the back of the clinic, where yet another nurse joined us. The three of them prepped me for admittance to the hospital. Each wearing a lavender tunic, they moved about the room as if their motions were choreographed. One checked my vitals, another prepped an IV, another looked up records. I knew each of them individually. Together they formed a SWAT team that was mesmerizing to watch.

A young orderly from the main hospital appeared at the foot of the bed, transferred me to a gurney, and shuttled me to a room in the cancer ward on the hospital's third floor. Unbeknownst to me, I had contracted a severe bacterial infection. The chemo at Overlake had weakened my immune system and I was slipping into sepsis, a condition the Mayo Clinic defines thus:

> *Sepsis is a potentially life-threatening complication of an infection. Sepsis occurs when chemicals released into the bloodstream to fight the infection trigger inflammatory responses throughout the body. This inflammation can trigger a cascade of*

changes that can damage multiple organ systems, causing them to fail. If sepsis progresses to septic shock, blood pressure drops dramatically, which may lead to death.

Anyone can develop sepsis, but it's most common and most dangerous in older adults or those with weakened immune systems. Early treatment of sepsis, usually with antibiotics and large amounts of intravenous fluids, improves chances for survival.[41]

The orderly rolled me into a room painted a deep reddish-brown, where a flat-screen LG television hung on the wall like a picture frame. A blue fabric couch stretched under the window matched by a recliner to its left. Despite my ashen pallor, I felt alive and alert. Minutes before, I had sauntered into Dr. Austin's clinic in my jeans and oxfords. I now found myself lying in a gown on a gurney after a NASCAR pit crew had transformed me from citizen to patient in under three minutes. Adrenaline surged.

The orderly moved me next to the bed. "Can you slide over?" he asked.

I sat up and shimmied from gurney to mattress. The orderly raised the plastic railings and left. Not long after, as the air settled, a female nurse entered and walked quietly up to the PC that perched atop a stand next to my bed.

"Still taking fluconazole?" she asked, her face glowing in

---

41   http://www.mayoclinic.org/diseases-conditions/sepsis/home/ovc-20169784

the light from the monitor.

"Yes," I replied, still feeling animated.

"When did you last take it?"

"This morning."

"Still taking Bactrim?"

"Yes."

"When did you last take it?"

"This morning," I repeated.

She walked through the remainder of my med list, and then moved to the standard litany of questions all nurses must ask when admitting a patient to a hospital (or at least they ask them at Swedish).

"Are you allergic to anything?"

"No."

"Do you smoke?"

"No."

"Does your religion preclude you from getting treatment?"

"No."

"Do you feel safe at home?"

I pictured Luke and Sofia landing sharp elbows and knees in my abdomen as they attacked me on the couch. Was I safe?

"Yes."

The nurse wrapped a plastic gray band snugly around my arm and latched the overlapping Velcro ends. My blood pressure registered low, 118 over 79, but within the range of normal . She pinched a stubby clothespin onto the end of my index finger to gauge the level of oxygen in my blood...100 percent. Next, she checked my temperature...102 degrees. Then she, too, left.

I looked around the room, focusing on nothing in particular, although I happened to notice the small, round analog clock hanging on the wall—5:30 p.m. All was quiet. The room, the hall, the entire floor. Nothing moved. Outside, the world was bustling. Inside, it was a city library at closing time. I dozed off.

When I awoke, night had fallen, and the clock read 8:45 p.m. I sensed someone next to the bed and turned my head to see yet another nurse. She had already placed the blood pressure cuff around my arm and initiated the check. Once again the cuff swelled until it felt tight around my bicep, paused, and began to let go.

"What are the numbers?" I asked after several seconds of silence, unable to see the monitor.

She said nothing so I sat up in the bed and turned to see the numbers for myself.

My blood pressure was a mere 69 over 28.[42] Eyes now wide open, I looked at the nurse and saw her face was frozen. I couldn't believe what I was seeing. Apparently, neither could she.

Those numbers are impossible...

A speaker blared, "We have a code blue in 4112.

A code blue."[43]

Holy shit! That's my room!

Three staffers materialized at the foot of my bed, looking back and forth from the monitor to me, monitor to me. The tall one said, "We need to get him to the ICU." Another darted out of the room. The third raised the end of the bed to elevate my feet above my head.

"How do you feel?"

"Fine—I feel fine," I replied, adrenaline now coursing through my body.

"Your blood pressure is very low, Mr. Harp," she told me in a rapid clip. "We're going to take you to the ICU so we can monitor you more closely."

Once again on a gurney, I rocketed through the halls, motored by a bald, muscled orderly. He rattled the contraption into an elevator, took me down one floor, and

---

42   I don't recall the exact numbers, but they were astonishingly low.

43   It might have been another color—not necessarily blue.

rolled me into a room that was almost identical to the one I had left. There, in the quiet of the ICU, the voltage in the air neutralized and my mind calmed so I could process my circumstances.

You've got to be kidding me! There's no way I'm going to die from low blood pressure, of all things. I mean, really? C'mon...not fucking low blood pressure! That's what's going to take me out after all this?

These weren't words of bravery, but rather of incredulity and, in some ways, anger. It was flight or fight, and I was going to fight, particularly if we weren't even talking about the school bully but just some punk I had never even considered.

Low blood pressure?

Little did I know what I was up against. It was indeed a rather intimidating bully. I had walked into Dr. Austin's office with a severe, systemic bacterial infection—sepsis—that deteriorated into septic shock, a medical meltdown during which blood pressure plummets.[44]

---

44   Per the National Institutes of Health (NIH): "Septic shock is a serious condition that occurs when a body-wide infection leads to dangerously low blood pressure. The affliction can affect any part of the body, including the heart, brain, kidneys, liver, and intestines. Septic shock is a medical emergency. In most cases, people are admitted to the intensive care unit of the hospital.

"Septic shock has a high death rate. The death rate depends on the patient's age and overall health, the cause of the infection, how many organs have failed, and how quickly and aggressively medical therapy is started.

Respiratory failure, cardiac failure, or any other organ failure can occur. Gangrene may occur, possibly leading to amputation." https://medlineplus.gov/ency/article/000668.htm

The hall bustled with nurses and attendees the next morning. A physician appeared at the foot of my bed. Tall and grave, he asked, "Do you have a power of attorney or living will?"

The power of attorney is a legal document that gives someone the ability to make health-care decisions on your behalf should you become mentally incapacitated— go into a coma, for example. A living will says explicitly what end-of-life treatment you will or won't allow if you are no longer able to communicate with doctors. If you don't want to be kept alive in a vegetative state, a living will would prevent that from happening, or the reverse if that's your wish.

The question took me off guard. "Yes, but I don't have a copy with me."

"You should have a copy on file with the hospital," he replied sternly.

Um...ok ...I'll get right on that.

Soon another physician appeared. This one was much younger, yet sober like his predecessor. "Do you have a living will or power of attorney?" he asked.

Now that I was hearing it for the second time within a matter of minutes, I took the question a little more seriously.

They think I'm going to die.

THINGS GET WEIRD

Everything appeared ordinary. Members of my immediate family lined the circumference of my room— my brother, my mom, Angela, the kids. All was dark save the blue luminescence of the television. We talked and laughed. And it felt heartening to have Luke and Sofia hop onto my bed with me. Soon, though, it was time to shut things down, so everyone said their goodbyes. Luke and Sofia gave me kisses as my family filed out of the room, leaving me alone with a television I wasn't even watching.

A moment later, an ICU nurse named Beatrice marched swiftly to the head of my bed, and, clearly hostile, pointed her index finger an inch from my nose. She spoke in a low and vicious whisper, barely able to contain her rage.

"Now that your peeps are gone, we have a new set of rules," she hissed, her spittle hitting my face. "One, you will not pee on the floor. Two, you will stay in your bed. Three, I will not clean up after any more of your messes!"

"What are you talking about?" I asked, surprised and indignant over the unfounded accusations.

I haven't been peeing on the floor. What is she talking about?

"You know *exactly* what I'm talking about," she retorted, pelting my face with more spittle.

"No, actually I don't."

Beatrice stood back and glared at me. A silver perm

billowed high on her head. She raised her finger and opened her mouth to say something, but instead she turned and vanished.

I was stunned. *Where the hell did that come from?*

When I awoke two hours later, both the sky outside and my room were dark, though yellow light fell through the doorway from the hall.

Beatrice reappeared. This time, she walked with a gentle gait to the head of my bed, placed her hands slowly on the guard rail, and lowered her face to mine as if she wanted to tell me a secret. Her vibe was altogether different.

"We need to get rid of a nurse," she told me in a hushed, conspiratorial tone. Pointing through the doorway, she identified a young Filipina woman, no older than twenty-five, seated at a maple desk in the hallway.

"She's incompetent. She must be fired."

I don't know what happened to the fiery, hostile woman who had come to my room moments before, but this Beatrice was friendly. She wanted my help. And her assertion that the young nurse needed to be fired for whatever reason seemed to make sense.

I nodded my head in assent.

"Good."

Minutes later, the alarm on the IV pump next to my bed went off.

Beep. Beep. Beep.

Serena, the young nurse whom Beatrice wanted fired, skated across my line of sight. Her shiny black hair tucked into a neat bun, her pretty face jeweled with cocoa eyes, she bent down to investigate the digital readout on the pump.

IV pump alarms are always going off in a cancer ward as bags of fluid run empty or IV lines get bent. The alarms are less a danger signal than a maintenance call. Most nurses can silence the alarms in a couple of clicks, but Serena struggled to get the thing to quiet down. I could tell she was growing frustrated.

"It's ok," I told her. "It happens."

"Thanks." She smiled.

Serena floated to the other side of the bed to take my blood pressure, yet she couldn't get the Velcro to hold. The cuff fell to the floor the moment it started to inflate.

"Can I help?" I asked.

"No. I've got it," she said nervously.

Serena gathered the paper cups and wrappers that had accumulated on the table next to me and deposited them in the garbage slot under the counter on the far side of the room.

And then she left. Without washing her hands.

Good hospitals are fanatical about requiring all staff to wash their hands before and after entering a patient's room to minimize the risk of spreading germs. The fact that Serena didn't wash her hands was a real no-no.

I guess Beatrice was right. She is kind of struggling a bit.

I somehow sensed that Beatrice wanted me to report Serena, but I never did. Still, Beatrice's plan succeeded. After Serena left, I fell asleep, only to be awoken by blue and red lights flashing brightly outside my window. I looked out and saw a uniformed policeman leading Serena to his parked cruiser. Her hands were cuffed behind her back. A cabal of hospital staff hidden in a shadow dotted with the orange glow of burning cigarettes watched as the officer placed his hand on top of Serena's head and guided her into the vehicle. Serena stared ahead, expressionless. Her eyes didn't blink.

The onlookers murmured among themselves while the plum uniforms they wore reflected the moonlight. One scoffed as the police car pulled away, tossing his cigarette butt to the ground. Two more cigarette butts arced through the air as the group turned and dispersed. And once again I slept.

The patrol car returned less than an hour later, only its lights were no longer flashing. An officer stepped out of the car and scanned the perimeter before grabbing the chrome handle on the passenger-side back door and pulling it open. Out stepped Serena, who moments later appeared at the foot of my bed, her face smoldering with anger. Brow furrowed, she marched with purpose to the IV pole and tapped furiously at the pump, making sharp clacking noises with her fingernails.

"I thought you weren't like them!" she fumed. "You're worse; you just pretended to be nice!"

She strode heatedly to the monitor on the other side of the bed and struck the power button to turn it off. She seized the pillow from under my head, punched it with both fists, jerked my head up, and stuffed the pillow back underneath.

"Comfy?" she demanded, her eyes burning black.

She whisked out of the room.

Time passed and I forgot about Serena. I imagine I slept, but I don't recall for certain. I do, though, remember when one of the nurses in the hallway, a bald, muscular male in his early thirties, suddenly began talking very loudly, almost shouting.

"This trip's going to be great!" yelled Tyson, with too much enthusiasm to sound genuine. His pale arms protruded from the short sleeves of his light green top as he lay back in his chair, feet on the desk.

"They're leaving tomorrow!" Beatrice shouted in reply, her tone as false. "I hear it's going to be amazing!"

"Heck, yeah!" Tyson responded. "I wish I were going!"

I knew right away something was up. *There's something going on here. They're trying to trick me into going on that trip!*

"I'm not going on your fucking trip!" I shouted.

Beatrice and Tyson stopped talking. Silence ensued. No

longer grinning, Tyson stood and walked out of my line of vision, though I could still hear him.

"This was a bad idea," he breathed quietly to Beatrice. "He knows."

They can't trick me. There's no way I'm getting on that plane.

"You fucks!" I screamed, now angry. I realized someone was standing in the room next to mine, listening to the conversation. A stranger in a black, pinstriped suit. *He* was the one trying to get me on the plane.

"I know who you are! Fuck you!" I yelled out. "I know what you're up to! I'm not going on your goddamn trip, asshole!"

A teenaged girl appeared in the doorway. Long brown hair framed her delicate, pale face. Her eyes were red from crying. I hadn't realized she was next door with the man. She was his daughter.

"I'm sorry," I said. "I wasn't yelling at you."

"I know."

Five men and women in mint-green hospital garb rushed into the room, surrounded my bed, and pinned me against the mattress using all their strength.

"Get off!" I screamed, lashing about in an attempt to break free. I looked directly at a staffer wearing wire-rimmed glasses, cocked my right knee, and kicked him in the chest as hard as I could, sending him backward, arms flailing. I screamed and cursed.

I awoke to find myself tethered by thick leather straps to a bedframe in the hospital basement, where a single incandescent bulb cast a weak, dingy pall over a shabby plywood workbench on the far wall.

"Unnghh!"

I couldn't lift my wrists more than two inches off of the mattress. Looking intently at my right hand, I pulled as hard as I could. Nothing. I tried to lift my head to see my feet, but couldn't. The straps holding my wrists to the frame wouldn't allow it.

A sheen of perspiration formed on my forehead. I began breathing rapidly. My mind raced in fear.

"Somebody let me out!" I shouted into the silent darkness.

A dark-haired man in a mauve nurse's uniform stepped into the light in front of the workbench.

"You kicked a girl," he said.

Huh?

I recognized his face. He had been assigned to care for me in the ICU. I recalled that he would whisper a blessing every time he left the room and that he was one of the staff standing outside when the police came for Serena. He knew Beatrice had conspired to get Serena fired and arrested! And I knew what a cadre of staff had done to Beatrice in retribution. They had carried Beatrice to a wooded area near the hospital's back parking lot where the grass grew high and light from the lampposts didn't reach. There, they had chained her to a rusty white bed frame, soaked her in gasoline, and burned Beatrice alive.

"Confess," he said softly. I noticed he had moved into the dark where I could no longer see his face. I sensed that he didn't want me to confess to anything having to do with Serena. He wanted me to confess something else, something deeper. He wanted me to admit a fault. Not a minor shortcoming, but something substantial.

Straining to think, I scanned the ceiling tiles, their edges brown with water damage, their surfaces dirty and gray with age.

Think! If you want out of this, it has to be real. You have to be honest. Don't hold back.

Finally, I felt an answer come to my lips and I shouted it out before I knew what it was. "I'm selfish!" I yelled, certain the nurse would appreciate the honesty. Apparently he did, because he walked silently to the side of my bed and unbuckled the strap holding my left wrist. He faded into the darkness.

One strap gone, three more to go...

The next thing I knew, I found myself back in the ICU, in a small room painted the thick orange color of a Creamsicle. The room was empty save for my bed. No furniture, no shelves, no sink. Just glowing orange walls.

A Dr. Rill, skeletal and grim, hunched over the head of

the bed so that he could reach under the mattress and punch me in the back.

Thwap.

It didn't hurt. He was just trying to intimidate me.

"I can get ten thousand!" I yelled.

I knew he wanted money but also knew I couldn't mention the word "dollars." We had to speak in code. I had twenty-five thousand dollars in the bank. That's it. If he wanted more, I was screwed, so I was low-balling. Ten thousand was my starting number.

If he didn't receive the money, Dr. Rill and the others would burn me alive, just as they had Beatrice.

Dr. Rill thumped the mattress again. "I think we can do better than ten thousand," he growled.

I looked up to see Dr. Rill's grimacing face. Next to him stood Sarah, a nurse I knew only by name, smiling because she enjoyed watching my torment. And my mother, still kindly but now in cahoots with the others. The three of them—Dr. Rill, Sarah, and my mother—had met in prison. Now they were extorting me.

I wrestled with the fact that my mother had been pretending all these years. That she was, in fact, a convict. How was that possible? She had been so kind and loving, yet now I find out it had all been a ruse. However, unlike Dr. Rill and Sarah, both of whom were displaying their violent natures, my mother showed empathy.

I tried to sit up in the bed, but Sarah slammed me back to the mattress with her muscular, tattooed arms, laughing. Prison had made her strong. "Don't think for a moment that I don't have practice keeping people like you from escaping!" she howled.

My mother started to caress my forehead. At first, Dr. Rill didn't notice, but when he did, he became angry.

"It's time, Sharon," he growled.

"He doesn't need to go," my mother responded calmly.

"Yes, he does!"

"No," replied my mother as she continued to stroke my head, secretly signaling to me that she was stalling Dr. Rill. As suddenly as it had appeared, gone was the glowing orange paint. Gone were Dr. Rill and Sarah. I was back in the hospital bed in the ICU. Sunlight fell through the large window to the far left, where my mother rocked in a chair, a book in her lap. All was quiet, but I still sensed danger. I knew that "they" still planned to torture me, most probably burn me to death as they had Beatrice, so I debated in my head: kill myself or die horribly?

I thought hard about how I could kill myself, but nothing came to mind. The room held no sharp objects. Obviously, I didn't have a gun. But there was the window.

I'll jump through the window.

The sharp lines of the room softened as I rolled the idea over and over in my head. I started to feel sad that it had come to this—sad that I had to end my life. Did this really need to happen? Was I certain?

I saw no other choice.

The room was still, the hallway outside empty. My mother rocked in her chair, engrossed in the pages of her book, oblivious to the plan I had hatched.

Now was the time. No going back.

Go!

I bolted from my bed onto the floor. The IV needle ripped out of my arm as I raced to the window, the tail of my gown flying behind me. My mother got to her feet and jumped in my way.

"No! No! No!" she screamed, her face adamant.

"Get out of my way!" I shouted.

I shifted to the right. She moved in tandem to block my path. I shifted left. She moved again, grabbed my shoulders, and leaned against me with all the weight she could muster.

Wow...she's pretty strong..."Move it!" I yelled again.

"No!"

"You're like a gazelle!" exclaimed Sarah, who suddenly grabbed me from behind in a reverse bear hug. "We're going to have to keep an eye on you!"

Angela: In the midst of Walt's hallucinations, Dr. Austin invited me to coffee, so the two of us made our way to the Starbucks in the hospital's cavernous marble entry. Dr. Austin's purpose? To share with me that it had come to the point where the treatment might have become more lethal than the disease. Dr. Austin felt she was killing Walt, although at the same time it wasn't clear whether Walt was trying to live or die. He was in agony, and Dr. Austin felt guilty. I was pretty stubborn in my position, though—that despite the suffering, I didn't think he wanted to go. And I believed he would pull through.

Dr. Austin and I agreed to press forward.

Years later, my mom revealed to me that even Walt's mom, who had once again flown in to be by our side, was having her doubts She never expressed these directly to me, but in retrospect it's a pretty wretched revelation. My mother-in-law is unbendingly optimistic by nature, and over the last several years she's demonstrated nothing but unwavering confidence in her son's ability to prevail despite the bleakest odds. I've come to rely on her positivity, so if she had doubts, that meant things were really grim. I chose to ignore the signs out of my own stubbornness and faith in Walt's invincibility.

Hours later, I woke to find my brother dozing in the room's one recliner. The sconces on the wall glowed a soft amber. A short, stocky nurse sat guard on a chair inside the doorway facing the two of us. The hospital had placed him there in case I made another try for the window.

"Porter..." I called out in a low voice from the bed. "Porter..."

My brother opened his eyes and looked at me from behind his glasses.

"Porter..."

"Yeah?"

"What time is it?"

"It's 2:05 in the morning."

The black hands on the wall clock indeed read 2:05. I closed my eyes and went back to sleep for several hours.

"Porter..." I whispered. "Porter..." Once again my brother opened his eyes to look at me. The clock now showed 2:06.

"Yes?"

"The clock hasn't moved," I told him, confounded by the fact that time was standing still.

"No, it hasn't," he said expectantly, as if I had something to add. Which I didn't, so I closed my eyes.

A long time later, I woke again.

"Porter..."

"Yes?" he answered, this time with mild alarm.

"Why is it only 2:08?"

Porter turned his head toward the nurse sitting guard,

who in response mouthed to him, "Go with it. You don't want to upset him."

Porter said nothing, and I passed out once again.

For two more days, I remained convinced that I was in grave jeopardy, but the acute paranoia lessened.

On morning rounds, Dr. Austin listened patiently as I tried to make her aware of the danger I was in, but I could barely form words, much less complete sentences.

"Call the police," I told Angela.

"I can call Edie. How would that be?"

"OK." I determined that Edie, a friend and physician, could protect me.

"Edie, come here," I whispered when she arrived the next morning, daylight filtering through the shades.

"What is it?" she asked.

I have to convince her. "Please stay" was all I could muster.

Edie would later comment that my eyes were as wide as soccer balls.

Over the next twenty-four hours, the paranoia drained and reality reclaimed my mind, though mild hallucinations continued. I held gripping conversations with myself, so compelling that I didn't want to stop talking even after I realized with disappointment that the conversations weren't real. Meanwhile, phantasms, vague colorful shapes with ill-defined edges, floated in the room.

"You had a break with reality," Dr. Austin explained when she saw me next.

That's embarrassing...

"You'd be surprised at how many people this happens to when they undergo the extremes you have. It's very common."

OK, that makes me feel better.

My delusions had been driven by a combination of heavy antibiotics, systemic bacterial infection, and confinement to the ICU. Medical literature refers to this condition as "ICU Psychosis": "A disorder in which patients in an intensive care unit (ICU) or a similar hospital setting may experience anxiety, become paranoid, hear voices, see things that are not there, become severely disoriented in time and place, become very agitated, even violent, etc. Organic factors including dehydration, hypoxia (low blood oxygen), heart failure (inadequate cardiac output); infection and drugs can cause or contribute to delirium."[45]

It turns out Beatrice, the nurse, was real, but she wasn't hostile and never schemed to have another nurse dismissed. And she wasn't burned alive in a field behind the hospital.

---

45   http://www.medicinenet.com/script/main/art.asp?articlekey=7769

Serena, too, was real, I later realized. But, of course, she wasn't incompetent, much less arrested at work.

I did scream and curse at what I imagined to be a stranger in the room next to mine, the one who was trying to manipulate me into going on an ominous plane ride. And the mystery man's daughter who showed up at my doorway in tears? That was actually Serena, and it was to her that I had apologized for all the yelling and profanity. A year later, when I went back to Swedish Issaquah with a fever, I was astonished to see Serena walk into my room.

Holy cow—she's real! "I'm so sorry about what happened," I said, the normal me.

"It's ok. When you apologized, I knew you weren't really like that," Serena responded. Still, once she left the room, she never returned. Either her shift ended or she asked the head nurse to be recused, and I certainly wouldn't have blamed her. I'm sure I had been scary to deal with.

I did try to hit a nurse, and in response several hospital staff strapped me to my bed with nylon restraints. According to Angela and my mother, Dr. Austin was livid when she found out.

"You did *what*?"

No one put me in the hospital's basement, however, nor was I asked to confess character flaws. No one extorted me for money. And my mom wasn't an imposter who had met Dr. Rill—a kind and patient infection specialist—in prison, and Sarah was a warm and lovely nurse, although indeed quite strong.

Angela: Walt did in fact leap out of bed and run to the window, hell-bent on crashing through it, though I doubt he would have made it through the double-paned glass. And it wasn't Walt's mom who blocked the way. It was me.

Walt had lost his marbles.

Sarah did call him a gazelle when she grabbed hold of him. Afterward, the hospital stationed a nurse outside Walt's room to keep an eye on him—and keep him away from the window.

I had indeed flummoxed my brother by asking him at several intervals over a period of seven minutes why the clock hadn't moved when, as I believed to be the case, I had slept for hours. I did work to convince friends who visited to understand the peril I was in. And I did ask Angela to call the police and couldn't formulate sentences to explain to Dr. Austin, Edie, or anyone else why I was at risk.

The male nurse who I imagined confessing to in the basement was real. And he did, in fact, whisper a blessing every time he left my room while I was under his care.

SPONGE BATH

My mother looked at me and said, "Don't get angry, but I need to tell you something. Your nurse wants to sprinkle holy water on your head. I told her that was fine."

"You what?" I said, both surprised and annoyed.

"I told her the holy water was ok."

I had asked my mother to not speak to medical staff on my behalf, as she was far too willing to agree to procedures that I didn't want or need. Or she simply confused things for everyone and prolonged conversations that didn't need to be. Plus, because she was spending hours and hours hovering over me—literally standing over my bed and waiting for me to ask for something—I had grown aggravated by her mere presence.

I know—not exactly something to be proud of, but I have to be honest.

I had nothing against the holy water. Who am I to turn down such a kind gesture? It was the meddling that made me crazy. The holy water was the last straw.

"Mom, I need you to leave."

"What? Right now?" she asked, scoffing. My mother is a kind woman, but you don't want to get her angry; and I could tell I had offended her.

"Yes." I couldn't take it anymore. "I'm sorry, but you do. Now."

Acquiescing but with her feelings bruised and anger rising, my mother packed her book bag and walked out. I would like to say that I wasn't relieved after she left, but, again, to be honest, I was.

Not much later, the nurse returned to take my vitals.

"Would you like a bath?" she asked with a light Spanish accent.

*Ooh...that sounds nice...*I hadn't bathed in days. "Yes, that would be great."

"I'll let Janessa know."

Crap.

Janessa, a large Jamaican woman in her late twenties, must have wrestled professionally in the WWF prior to becoming a nurse. I didn't want her to touch me. She was both gruff and impatient. The thought that she should have been fired a long time ago had crossed my mind more than once. While all the other nurses were gentle and kind, Janessa was ill-tempered.

She walked into my room frowning and told me to undress, because we were going to the shower (so much for a sponge bath). So I disrobed and followed her into the private bathroom. Silver handrails punctuated the brown tile covering the walls and a plastic bench for the disabled jutted out from underneath the showerhead. Janessa turned on the water and, after waiting for it to get hot, ordered me to sit on the bench. Using a sheet of clear adhesive plastic she covered the Hickman line hanging from my right pectoral, which, as you may recall, fed directly through my chest into my vena cava. At constant risk of bacterial contamination, the tube and its entry point into the skin had to be kept dry at all times, hence the plastic.

At first, the water was comforting, and I started to feel relaxed and fresh as Janessa ran the nozzle over me. But the euphoria didn't last. Janessa began scrubbing with a rough washcloth. Hard. Really hard. I wanted it to stop immediately but felt obligated to go through with the "bath" since I had agreed to it. I toughed it out for several minutes as Janessa brushed my skin raw before surrendering.

"I think that's enough..."

For Janessa, it wasn't. She continued to scrape each part of my body at least three more times. She also scrubbed the plastic shield covering the Hickman line. The hole where the tubes entered my chest began to bleed.

Oh shit.

"Stop!" I said firmly, pointing to the blood now oozing underneath the plastic. Janessa paused. Even she knew that wasn't good.

At last. It's over.

Janessa grabbed a pair of white towels and beat me dry before calling an IV nurse to come re-dress the Hickman. And I vowed to never again agree to a "sponge bath."

Because I had spent three weeks in a hospital bed, much of it delusional, I had lost most of my leg strength. As a result, I could barely stand, much less walk. I was at enormous risk of falling, so the staff alarmed my bed to keep me there. I was only allowed up if someone was in the room to monitor me. Because of the alarm, the moment I slid even one of my feet off the mattress, a horn blared. Sitting up on my knees would also sound the alarm, and only a staffer could stop the obnoxious noise. My bed became a jail cell. Getting up to go to the bathroom became an ordeal.

I dreaded having to call the nurses' desk each time I needed to pee, which was easily four or five times a night given the amount of fluids flowing into my arms through IV tubes. Don't get me wrong. The nurses were super diligent, hardworking, and as responsive as they could be, but they were shorthanded. I'd sometimes have to wait a good fifteen minutes for someone to come to my assistance— an eternity when you have to go, particularly when you're suffering from what doctors refer to as "urgency." Each time I felt urgency rising, I would scramble to find the remote that was constantly lost in the various nooks and crannies of my bed and, once in hand, press the magic red button to call a nurse.

Press.

Wait...

Wait...

Wait...

Press the call button again.

Wait...

Wait...

Wait...

Press, press, press.

Finally, a good ten minutes later, a xylophone would sound overhead—*Ding, dong, ding!*—followed by a friendly female voice.

"May I help you?" crackled over the speaker.

"I need someone to turn off the bed alarm so I can go to the bathroom." I spoke loudly, not because I was angry but because I wanted to be sure she heard me—the room was vast, the acoustics terrible.

"OK, I'll find your nurse." *Click.*

Wait...

Wait...

Wait...

Wait...

Wait...

Wait...

Inevitably the wait would drag on so long that I would have no choice but to consider alternatives. There were always one or more plastic urinals hanging from the side of the bed (looking deceptively like water bottles). Unfortunately, I needed to stand up to use them, or at least get on my knees on the mattress. Either movement would set off the alarm.

Why is this taking so long?

I guess I could have gotten out of the bed. The alarm would have gone off, but so what? Someone would have come to my room, and I would have explained what happened. That's all. For whatever reason, I felt that setting off the alarm was out of the question—I guess when at the mercy of a hospital, I feel more obliged to follow rules. I had to stay in bed, and the only way to pee in bed without triggering the alarm was to urinate into one of the bottles while lying on my back, a risky operation to say the least. So I would lie back, grab one of the plastic bottles, and stuff both my penis and scrotum into the opening at the top in an effort to form a hermetic seal in hopes of preventing urine from leaking all over my gown...which I only learned to do effectively after several failed attempts. During those initial tries, I could feel the gown grow damp as I released. Too late to turn back, I would have to stay on course despite the growing wetness. Probably a third of what I intended for the bottle would actually make it in. The rest drenched both me and my bed covers.

Without fail, moments after I had soaked gown and bed, I would hear a voice at the doorway.

"Can I help you?"

"Can we please disarm the bed?"

I needed to regain the ability to walk, so Carlos, a burly physical therapist equal to me in height, came to my room daily to help me get up and move around. I looked forward to our sessions as a break from lying bedridden. My only challenge with Carlos was that he was too conservative. Even though he was doing his job (and doing it well), I always felt as if he wasn't giving me enough leash to run with, which was frustrating.

"Stand up from the bed," he instructed one day. I rose as slowly as I could, yet his face still showed worry.

"Careful! Careful!" he cautioned. "Now take a rest." We waited for a full minute.

"All right. Good. Now I want you to walk three steps toward me." I hobbled forward, concentrating on my balance.

"Careful! Not too fast!"

Upon reaching Carlos, I grabbed his shoulders to steady myself.

"OK. Great. Now let's walk to the counter...Place your hands on top. Good."

Another full minute of rest.

"Raise your left knee...drop it. Raise your right knee... drop it."

I marched in place and then made an attempt at light squats.

"Excellent. Now take another rest and we'll head to the hallway."

Carlos snatched a wide, white canvas belt from atop the

counter and wrapped it around both my waist and his, tethering us together like mountain climbers on Everest. Carlos walked behind me so that his weight would keep me standing should I falter. I was already wearing standard hospital-issue anti-slip socks, so all I needed before we embarked on our journey into the hallway was a face mask to protect me from germs. Carlos handed one to me.

Gown tied in back to cover bare bottom—check. Tethered to Carlos—check. Face mask—check. Ready to venture forth!

Safety rails made of dark wood ran along both sides of the hallway. A light parquet covered the floor.

"I want you to hold the railing," Carlos directed.

"OK."

"Now take a step forward."

I moved one foot.

"Hold on...hold on! Go slower."

I'm barely moving, Carlos.

"How are you feeling?"

"Fine."

"OK...three more steps...Slowly! Slowly!"

Good lord. We could go faster than this.

"Rest! Rest!"

This is killing me.

"Three more steps and then I want you to turn around so we can go back. Don't move too fast!"

Young with long blond hair, Kathryn, the other physical therapist, who alternated with Carlos, took a far more liberal approach the next day. Sure, like Carlos she utilized the canvas safety belt, but she didn't tether us together; rather, she wrapped the belt around my waist and held it at the small of my back with one hand. She couldn't have weighed more than 120 pounds, so I wasn't sure how she planned to hold me up if I fell, but that didn't matter.

"Ready?" Kathryn asked.

Indeed, I was. "Let's do it."

I shuffled to the hallway with great intent and, once there, touched my fingers to the railing ever so lightly so as not to over-rely on it. I proceeded to step forward as quickly as I could without face-planting. As my confidence grew, so did my speed, from snail to turtle, from turtle to toddler, from toddler to...standing still to catch my breath.

We hiked far. Very far. We looped the floor twice, and then pushed through swinging doors that led into a glass walkway connecting two buildings thirty feet above the ground. Between the sun pouring through the glass and my vision starting to blur, I could barely see. Soon I felt lightheaded. Moving patterns formed before my eyes, as if I were looking at the world through a kaleidoscope. Kathryn continued to walk behind me, canvas belt in hand.

"Do you need to stop?" she asked, noting I was slowing

down.

"I'm dizzy. I don't think I can walk anymore. I think I need to sit."

"I'll find you a wheelchair," she said, but there were none to be found. We were completely alone, the hallway empty save for the sunlight.

"Okay...maybe you should sit on the floor." Kathryn stood behind me and put her arms around my waist. All I wanted to do was sit on the floor. I needed to recover. Just then, a tall orderly in green garb came through the doors at the far end of the hallway. He was pushing an empty wheelchair. A miracle.

Once we returned to my room and I climbed back in bed, I reveled in silence. *Furthest walk yet! Yes!*

My vision remained blurry regardless of whether I was sitting in bed or out walking. Even my squinting didn't bring things into focus. When I finally gained enough strength to walk the hallways alone, I found that I couldn't make out the faces of any of the hospital staff I passed. I smiled at everyone, hedging my bets that I might know them.

Tiny blisters and cuts covered the inside of my mouth, thanks to all the chemicals I had been subjected to.[46] *Any* food item triggered immense pain. Fortunately, the medical staff provided me with what they aptly called "magic mouthwash," a thick liquid containing lidocaine,

---

46   This may have been an aftereffect of the chemo at Overlake, I'm not sure.

topical pain medication with the taste and consistency of Pepto-Bismol. A capful numbed my mouth long enough for me to shovel down a cup of egg salad or Cream of Wheat without searing burn. Bland and creamy was good. Spicy or textured set my mouth on fire.

One afternoon, I tried to eat a grape Popsicle, thinking the cold would soothe my mouth. Instead, the icy temperature caused the sores to erupt. Eyes shut, I rocked back and forth in bed until the anguish subsided.

The hospital kitchen closed at 8 p.m. If I got hungry after that, I was out of luck, except for the foodstuff the hospital kept for patients in refrigerators on the floor: juice, applesauce, ice cream, pudding, and sometimes yogurt. All of it was sugary, none of it was savory. I ate so much applesauce that I dreamt of workers in red flannel picking apples in the orchards of Eastern Washington. The pudding was flat-out cloying. Having lost so much weight over the preceding weeks, I could afford the calories, but I could only take so much sugar. I wanted salt. A sandwich. Another cup of egg salad. Anything but pudding or applesauce.

On one especially long night as I lay awake at 1 a.m., I was hungry yet could not fathom ingesting yet another sugary substance. I pressed the call button on a whim.

"How may I help you?" a woman's voice answered.

"Is Francine available? I need to speak with her."

"I'll let her know."

Five minutes later Francine, a nurse, walked into my room.

"You wouldn't by chance have anything salty to eat, would you?" I asked.

"As a matter of fact, I do," Francine replied with a smile. "I brought pretzels to work today. Would you like some?"

"Yes!"

Sure, pretzels would be salty (yes!), but clearly my cerebral cortex had not fully parsed the scenario. I soon discovered that the handful of small pretzel sticks that Francine brought me turned to razor blades in my mouth. I found my way around that by sucking each of the precious baked delicacies until they softened into mealy pretzel paste. *Salty* mealy pretzel paste.

Heaven.

The next night, Angela brought the kids to see me. Luke marched into the room, holding a pair of Mylar balloons filled with helium and decorated with the words "Happy Birthday." Sofia carried a large red envelope with a card inside.

"Happy birthday, Daddy!" the kids shouted in unison, giggling as they ran to my bed.

I was surprised and happy to see them.

"Hi, guys! Come over and give your daddy a kiss!"

Luke and Sofia placed their small arms around my neck and pressed their lips to my cheeks. I turned my head toward Angela and smiled appreciatively.

"Thanks, schwee." (Not to go overly cutesy on you, but "schwee" is shorthand for "sweetie.")

Luke and Sofia danced about the room, laughing. Angela walked over to the couch by the window and set her bag down.

"How are you feeling?" she asked brightly. I didn't feel the need to manufacture a reply, so I told the simple truth.

"Tired."

"I'm sorry to hear that. We just wanted to say happy birthday!"

"I know—that's so sweet of you guys. I love it." Which I did.

But there was no getting Sofia and Luke to settle down. It wasn't that they were misbehaving. They're actually both awesome kids and very well-behaved. But at five and eight, what do you do in a small hospital room empty of toys other than chase your sibling and scream and laugh? There was only so much for them to be curious about and investigate. It's not like an IV pump is particularly captivating. Not surprisingly, after a short time, boredom set in.

As fatigued as I was, I felt the need to connect. Here they were, my children, whom I hadn't seen for weeks. Of course, I'm supposed to have a special moment, right? Isn't that what parents do with their kids after they've been apart for an extended period?

"Lukie!" I called out. "Lukie!"

"Yes, Baba?" he answered sweetly.

"C'mere."

Luke ran over to the side of the bed. I could see his tennis shoes were fraying in the front.

Time for new shoes..."What'd you do at school today?"

"Not much. We did a lot of math and then at free time I played soccer with the fifth graders."

"Awesome—did you score any goals?"

"Yes."

Dang. Remember not to ask questions that can be answered yes or no. You'll never get any conversation going that way. "Have you been helping Mommy at home?"

"Yes."

Ugh. Try again. "Who have you been playing with?"

"We went to Logan and Hannah's house last night."

Okay. You got a full sentence. Keep going. You need to make this visit count. They haven't seen their father in ages.

Doing my best to engage him, I set aside the fatigue and continued to ask Luke questions, while noting someone had put gel in his hair.

Did Angela do that?

Soon, though, I had to give in. It's not that Luke wasn't dynamic. I was tired. It was too much work. There was no way I was going to be able to switch my attention over to Sofia and try to engage her in conversation as well.

"You guys want to watch TV?" I asked.

"Yes!" Luke and Sofia shouted in unison.

"Okay—let's go to the big space outside. They have an awesome TV out there."

Luke and Sofia ran out of the room and down the hall to the ward's expansive sitting area, where large colorful, modern paintings, several of which I wanted to own, adorned the walls. On the oversized television, Richard Dawson was calling out top survey answers for *Family Feud* contestants.

There had better be something better than this.

Of course, there wasn't.

It's funny how you can't force a "moment, which, of course, doesn't matter with your kids. They were happy to see me, and I them. That's all we needed.

"Honey..." I whispered to Angela as Sofia and Luke shared a chair, watching some program I didn't recognize. "I'm pretty tired...I think I'm going to go back to bed." Angela smiled. Even though the visit had lasted all of twenty minutes, I saw that she understood. We're family, we love each other, and I would be home soon enough.

Angela: I understood his limited stamina, but couldn't help but be disappointed. A "Daddy visit" required a ton of coordination and energy. And we all felt giddy in anticipation. It was inevitable that the visit couldn't live up to my expectations.

HOME

Nearly a month after I had shown up in her clinic on the brink of sepsis, Dr. Austin discharged me from the cancer ward at Swedish Hospital, where I had lost touch with reality and almost died. I went back to our house on Mercer Island weak but free of infection and fever. There, I barely had the strength to get off of the couch, much less the energy to make meals for myself. Luckily, my mother stayed the entire month of October and then some to take care of me. The soft, buttery scrambled eggs and rich, creamy mac and cheese she made me were delicious and comforting, not to mention tolerable given that I still needed the magic mouthwash. At first, my mother would even liquefy the mac and cheese in a blender so that it would go down easier.

Angela: I felt so relieved Walt's mom had come to help. Honestly, I needed the break. His mom's coming was a godsend.

Even though I had left the hospital, my medication regimen didn't decrease. At discharge, the staff handed me an IV pole, tubing, alcohol wipes, disposable gloves, and bags and bags of antibiotics to infuse hour after hour. Morning, noon, night. A home care nurse taught me how to arrange the tubing and operate the battery-powered IV pump, a sensitive process given that I had to take great measures to avoid sullying *anything* with bacteria. *Everything* had to be kept *perfectly* antiseptic. That meant constantly changing out tubes and sanitizing the entire planet with alcohol wipes. I grew adept at the mechanics of home infusion, but it remained an arduous chore.

Kind of miss those nurses doing all this for you, huh?

Neuropathy from the chemo had left my fingers numb, yet I still managed to perform the necessary fine manipulations required to transact home infusion. I dragged the IV pole with me about the house while it slowly dripped medication through the Hickman into my chest. I watched TV, napped, read, did anything to pass the endless hours of infusion. I spent a lifetime at the kitchen table, shirtless with my scrawny, pale chest reflecting light from the flood lamps in the ceiling, assembling and dismantling infusion equipment. Empty IV bags, paper, plastic, empty foil wrappers, and vials of sodium iodine and heparin sullied the table as well as the far reaches of the house. Endless detritus.

A few days into my new life at home, Anupam—my boss and the CEO of the start-up where I worked—gave me a call.

"How are you feeling?"

"Tired, but good. Glad to be home."

"I was wondering if I could come over to see you."

That's nice of him.

"Want to swing by tomorrow afternoon, say, at 2 p.m.?"

"Perfect. See you then."

Cool.

The next day, I took off my ratty fleece and donned a pink Oxford to add some color to my otherwise gray pallor. I didn't want to look cadaverous in front of Anupam, not that he would have judged.

Angela: Walt at that point had lost nearly forty pounds. There's a haunting picture of him with me and the kids celebrating his coming home where he looks a bit like a Holocaust survivor. I recall our good friend Robyn coming to see him at home for the first time. She later told me how absolutely stunned she was by how gaunt he was.

"You look nice," my mother said as I slowly descended the stairs.

At 2 p.m., the doorbell rang. I opened the door and was happy to see a familiar face.

"Come in! Great to see you!" I greeted Anupam, who joined me at the kitchen table, which I had cleared of trash in anticipation of my visitor. It turned out he had come largely because he had important and sensitive news to share—one of the company's key executives had decided to leave.

"I've set up a conference call for tomorrow morning with the leadership team so we can discuss," Anupam told me.

"Okay—I can make it."

"You sure?" he asked. "You're up for it?"

Umm...yes...I really miss work. "Of course."

"Hey! Good to hear your voice!" went the chorus on the phone the next morning, a sunny Saturday. The familiarity of my colleagues felt warm and good. A week later, compelled to show I was still in the game, I decided to attend the company board meeting, something I would normally do. Noting my frail appearance, the company's lead board member asked Anupam afterward whether he was pushing me too hard to return to work. Of course he wasn't. And Anupam wasn't so happy with my surprise appearance and the unwarranted admonishment.

I apologized and stayed home after that.

Angela: Walt wanted so badly to get back to "normal." He hated not being able to work and thus pushed beyond where he should have. That said, I still believe in part it's his drive that has kept him alive. Walt would call that magical thinking, but I believe it regardless.

The ongoing maintenance chemo made me anemic. As a result, the simple act of standing left me dizzy. Every time I walked into my house, I had to stop after a few steps to rest my head on a shelf, stair rail, or the kitchen island—a condition that forced me to proactively map out strategic paths. Occasionally I'd simply black out and fall, hitting my head. A frightened Angela ended up buying a blood pressure cuff to keep an eye on my condition.

I also came down with an intractable case of hiccups. *Again*. They would not stop. Seriously. At their worst, the convulsions came mere seconds apart.

Hic...hic...hic!

The hiccups would build and build until I vomited in the kitchen sink or the toilet. And the cycle would begin again.

Hic...hic...hic!

Dr. Austin prescribed medications known to relieve chronic hiccups, but none of them worked. Concerned that something might be amiss with my stomach, she sent me to a gastroenterologist at a branch of Swedish in downtown Seattle.

Angela's mom, Alice, once again drove me to my appointment. When we arrived, she rolled down the ramp to the cement cavern that was the parking garage and found a spot three floors below. Once out of the car, we hadn't walked fifteen feet before I passed out and hit the ground.

At age seventy, Alice was healthy (and still is), but not strong enough to lift my 170 pounds. Fortunately, I came to and rose to my feet. We walked a bit further and *boom!* Down again. I tried to stand up.

"No, no. You stay sitting," Alice cautioned. "You need a wheelchair." Several cars over, a woman had seen me fall. She walked over in her heels to where I sat on the hard floor.

"Are you alright?" she asked.

"Yes," I replied. "Just a little anemic."

"Let me get some help."

The woman walked to the elevator, where a folded wheelchair happened to rest against the wall, abandoned. She brought it over, and I pulled myself in. Alice girded herself, gripped the handles, and pushed me forward. We found our way to the elevators and then to the office of a Dr. Havi, the gastroenterologist Dr. Austin had recommended. Alice and I explained to the nurse in charge what had happened in the garage. It turns out my blood pressure had once again fallen dangerously low, although not to the degree of severity it had been when I was rushed to the ICU at Swedish.

"You're extremely dehydrated," said the nurse. "We need to get some fluids into you before Dr. Havi can do the endoscopy."

Shit...that's going to take forever. Normally it took a liter of fluid a good two hours to drip into my arm, and I had forgotten my iPhone. I was destined to die of boredom.

"I hear you're a little dehydrated," said another nurse jokingly as he walked in. "No worries. We'll fix that. We're going to make this go fast using a trick I learned in the field when I was in the Marines," he told me with a wink and left the room. He came back with the tallest IV pole I'd ever seen. Rather than the usual five-ish feet in height, this one was more like twelve. I don't know how he cobbled it together, but the thing towered.

He smiled. "Higher height, faster flow."[47]

The bag drained in a mercifully short thirty minutes.

Thank God.

A female nurse in her forties walked into the room after the Empire State Building of IV poles had finished its work. "Mr. Harp, we're ready," she said in a friendly, professional tone. An orderly appeared and had me slide onto a gurney. He rolled me into an operating room lit ever so slightly, as if it were a romantic restaurant.

"I'm going to give you some medicine that will make you sleepy," said one of the technicians.

"Give him two milliliters," instructed Dr. Havi from the far end of the room. He was leaning against a counter with his arms crossed, projecting smoldering impatience. I didn't like the negativity he emanated.

Theoretically, anyone can undergo an endoscopy without sedation. That said, the humane thing to do is to make the patient semiconscious before the doctor shoves a ribbed

---

47   I'm not sure if this statement represents accurate physics—it's been a long time since high school—but it's honestly what he was going for with the mega-tall IV pole, which I loved him for inventing.

fire hose with a camera on the end down his gullet. I have high tolerance for Versed, the medication the nurse had told me would make me sleepy. With only two milliliters of Versed, I would be wide awake for the entire procedure.

One nurse fed the anesthetic through the IV in my arm while the others made small talk. Meanwhile, Dr. Havi stared silently at the operating table, a sullen look on his face.

Interesting that he doesn't engage with the nurses. Maybe the banter isn't compelling.

"Let's get started," Dr. Havi commanded sternly, minutes after the Versed was administered.

I'm not sedated in the slightest.

For whatever reason, though, I didn't speak up.

Dr. Havi crammed a ribbed metal hose the diameter of a quarter down my throat.

"Relax," he said.

"Urgh...! Urgle...gulk...!"

On the nearby monitor, I could see the moist pink insides of my esophagus as the camera dived deep into my gastrointestinal tract. Not the most comfortable experience, but I liked watching what amounted to the Discovery Channel in 4D (See it! Feel it!). It was frustrating, though, to later learn that the results revealed nothing that would be causing the chronic hiccups. It seemed I was stuck with them.

In fact, I dealt with my hiccups, apparently a side effect from all the systemic chemo and antibiotics, for nearly two years. On for two weeks, off for a few days. On for two weeks, off for a few days. I had to learn to live with it, as one would a limp or a bad back.

At my office, I often had to pause mid-sentence to hiccup, for which I kept apologizing. "Sorry—bear with me." And the only way I could get a break from the relentless onslaught of painful hiccups was to, well, put my fingers down my throat and force myself to throw up and then lie flat on my back. I could get as much as an hour's break that way.

I'd basically become bulimic. Sounds like a joke but, honestly, I was concerned that I was becoming addicted to self-induced vomiting.

Over time, my voice grew hoarse because of the abrasion caused by the ongoing regurgitation. During one of my check-ins even Dr. Austin remarked that my voice had become raspy.

Nothing addressed the hiccups. Well-intentioned people would ask me whether I had tried this remedy or that.

"Drink water backward."

"Stand on your head and hold your breath."

"Run a plastic tube up your nose and out your mouth and floss with it." *Seriously.* A doctor actually did that to me. Twice. (He was well-intentioned).

Each time someone proffered a new cure for hiccups, I would politely explain that I had tried that approach. Because I had. There were no home remedies left that I hadn't attempted.

"That must be terrible!" people would say. Sure— conceptually. But, honestly, cancer is endurance. You just deal. The convulsions in my diaphragm became part of my new normal. People around the world face much, much worse. The mind adjusts.

After many months without a solution, Dr. Austin, who by this time was family, happened across research stating it was possible to treat chronic hiccups by killing one of the two phrenic nerves that make the diaphragm function. With hope in my heart, I went to see a qualified surgeon right away. On the first go, he put one of my phrenic nerves to sleep. When that didn't achieve the desired results, he went back in and wiped it out. Afterward, the hiccups continued, but fluoroscopy (motion x-ray) showed that my diaphragm was now steady on one side while the other side continued to convulse.

Halfway there! I was overjoyed.

Given our partial success, the surgeon and I decided to take out the other phrenic nerve and finish the job. Unfortunately, or perhaps *fortunately*, a colleague advised him that killing off the second phrenic nerve would restrict my ability to breathe. I would require the use of a breathing machine at night. Which would be horrific.

In 2014, I went to see another gastroenterologist whom Dr. Austin recommended, this time for reasons not having to do with the hiccups. This doctor suggested I try a different combination of the anti-hiccup medicines I'd used in the past. Same meds, different combination. I held back from rolling my eyes and smiled—hers was a kind gesture. Despite my doubts, I decided to give it a try anyway. And incredibly—beautifully, mercifully—my hiccups vanished.

Angela: The hiccups were as pernicious as the cancer. Horrible to watch. I saw how Walt simply dealt with them—didn't get bogged down—but I couldn't imagine what he was going through. And I wanted to protect him, concerned that his hiccups would make others uncomfortable. Sofia, then barely six years old, told me she was grossed out each time she found bits of vomit lingering in the toilet.

Let's pause here. Can you imagine...two years of chronic diaphragm convulsions so disruptive that at times you could barely complete a sentence and from which you could only get a temporary break by making yourself throw up. And then...they're suddenly gone!

I'm a big believer in putting things in the past. Once that horrible flu you've been suffering from goes away, it becomes a distant memory. All the misery simply evaporates as if it was never there. That's human nature, and that is what happened to me. My chronic hiccups were such an odd, awful thing to endure, yet now they are a distant memory.

NO CURE, NOVEMBER 2012

I was sitting in an exam room in Dr. Austin's clinic, no more than three feet from her, for what was supposed to be a routine follow-up. Eight weeks had passed since the hallucinations in the ICU, the magic mouthwash, the sponge bath-gone-wrong—all now faded into the archives of my mind.

This conversation with Dr. Austin, though, stood front and center, like a suitcase full of explosives. It had my attention.

"The leukemia will come back," Dr. Austin said softly but unequivocally, "and there's no cure at this point."

Wow. It doesn't get clearer than that.

Dr. Austin had set a pin on the map. There was no guessing or mistaking its location. We had reached the end of potential treatments.

Every neuron in my brain was standing at the ready. But I wasn't caving on the inside. I was simply processing the information, which couldn't have been more straightforward. It was 1 + 1 = 2.

"*When* will it return?"

Dr. Austin hesitated. "The median survival rate is nine months."

I flipped a calendar in my head. If I took nine months as an average, even though she said median, not mean, that meant I probably had until June of the following year to live.

"For the moment you're in remission, else we'd be having a very different conversation. I'd be telling you to get your things in order."

She does not mince words.

"And I'd be suggesting that if there's anything you've wanted to do in life that you haven't, you should go do it."

I marveled at her candor. This was a whole new dialog. *We're really here. This is it.*

"I want you to see a former colleague of mine at the SCCA, a Dr. Kyzov," Dr. Austin continued. "He's working on an early trial that might be relevant. I told him you'd be reaching out."

Angela and I never actually saw Dr. Kyzov, but instead spent a good thirty minutes with a junior member of his team. We sat together in a small room at the SCCA, looking up at him leaning against an exam table as he held forth. In his hand, he had a blue piece of paper on which were printed the numbers one through five. Each number was associated with a definition of one of five stages of patient decline from leukemia. Stage one equated to perfect condition. Stage five was, well, dead. The researcher told me he was surprised to find me so close to a one. After reading my medical history, he'd expected me to be a four.

I was proud of my resiliency, though I knew I really had nothing to do with it. My body happened to be tenacious. Perhaps it helped that I'm optimistic, that friends and family prayed for me, that I'm determined, that I work through pain, that I push myself. That said, I believed—and still believe—my survival depended primarily on the skill of the doctors and nurses who cared for me, the state of medical science, and—as much as I hate to say it and had difficulty accepting it—luck. Certainly it wasn't me who got me to a two.

I respect that others may believe otherwise. Passionately so. That there are things we—or higher powers—can do to influence cancer outcomes. Which may very well be the case. Not making an argument here. Definitely not discouraging belief in the power of prayer or positive attitude or nontraditional approaches to cancer prevention or treatment. Not by any stretch. Just sharing an honest account of my thought process at the time.

In the end, it turned out my case wasn't right for the trial, but that's not the information that stuck with me after that day. It was something the young doctor said and the way he said it.

Looking both Angela and me directly in the eyes, he said: "It's a *certainty* the leukemia will come back."

Sure, Dr. Austin had said the same thing, only this man stated it so unflinchingly and with such emphasis on the word "certainty" that all hope drained. No more speaking in "ifs." No more hypotheticals. The leukemia was coming back, and that would be that.

Angela was mesmerized by the fact that the doctor had read the entirety of my medical record, a five-inch stack of papers. While she didn't recall the poignancy of the physician's unsparing proclamation of impending death, she does remember the fact that he had assumed I would be a four, not the two that I was.

I don't know how other people feel when they are told they only have a short period to live. At the time, I only knew what I had seen in movies and on television.

Do I empty the bank account? Maybe go skydiving or take the family to Java or climb K2? Quit my job and navigate Antarctica on skis?

The fact of the matter is I didn't want to do any of that. I wanted *normal*. I wanted home. I wanted to spend time with Angela, Luke, and Sofia. I wanted to go to work. And even if I didn't enjoy work, it's not like I could have quit. Fantasies remain fantasies when there are bills to pay. I did, though, splurge. I took Angela to Hawaii two weeks later. No shopping for discounts. I bought the tickets and made reservations at one of the nicest resorts on the Big Island. I remember sitting at a small table waiting for my wife to join me on the large outdoor patio where nearby the restaurant had placed the breakfast buffet on white linen. I drank fresh island coffee and savored the tropical aroma. Glancing surreptitiously at the people sitting at the other tables around me, I wondered if this was a run-of-the-mill vacation for them. For us it was an extravagance, that's for sure.

I took the family to Australia for two weeks as the deadline drew nearer. *That* was a bucket-list move, I'll admit, but my purpose was to build memories with the kids. I hired a travel planner, something I had only done once before (for my honeymoon with Angela to Puerto Rico while we were still students in New York), and made choices based on want, not cost. I *never* did that.

"I have less than a 10 percent chance of being here in three months," I told my good friend Kevin, who ended up working with me at the start-up under Anupam. It was just fact. I said the same to my good friend and former college roommate Steve, when we were driving back to my house after target shooting at a local indoor gun range. Steve had flown from New York to visit me post-apocalypse at Swedish.

The facts of my situation actually felt fantastical. I was free-falling and there was nothing to grab onto. Yet, for whatever reason, I didn't feel fear. I was simply observing fate unfold.

PART III:
WHERE'S THE EXIT?

MITAD: JUNE 10, 2014

I had been kidnapped by the curator of a torture museum in rural Virginia. She had put me in a prison cell in the darkest region of the old sandstone building where no one could find me, particularly since I hadn't told anyone I was going there.

Somehow I escaped and swore with all sincerity I'd never enter the State of Virginia again.

I lay abandoned on a hospital gurney outside the elevator bank in the basement of a city hospital. Everything was dark save for a few far-off fluorescent lights blinking in the tiled ceiling.

"Someone get over here now and take care of him!" It was Beverly, a friend of mine from work. Brazen and confident, she had come back to save me from purgatory.

I knew I could count on her.

I sat at a large, round wooden table in the dining room of a medieval castle. My legs felt incredibly heavy. My mother told the blond-haired man next to me to add more lead to the weight that was already sewn into the legs of my pants, which he did immediately.

Why would you do that, Mom? I can't move my legs!

A Christmas fire flickered playfully in the white hearth in the living room. A kettle full of large eggs in boiling water hung over the fire. The big question on everyone's mind: what's in the eggs? Were they male or female? I wanted to go downstairs to partake in the holiday festivities but I was too tired, and the carpeted bedroom nestled on the second floor only made me want to stay put that much more.

Days passed and the eggs cracked open. Inside were five pale-pink baby pigs, males and females, with eyes shut tight. They were dead. A motionless, floating litter.

I sat on an aluminum chair in an empty dining room in a nursing home, spooning tasteless brown pudding into my mouth. No one knew I was there. Not my family, not my friends, not anyone. I had disappeared into the system, left to wither anonymously in a shabby low-rise facility in Queens. Panicked, I converted to Judaism and suddenly found myself in a warm home surrounded by loved ones. Not my family, but people I knew and felt close to.

"Mitad," said the woman in the flowered skirt. Shiny black bangs fell from the white handkerchief tied around her head. "Mitad" is Spanish for "half." Our captor had ordered Angela, Luke, Sofia, and me to be forced into pants that were cut off and sewn shut halfway down the leg, meaning we'd have to wear the pants kneeling and, from that point on, hobble about trapped on our knees.

The idea of it horrified me. I pictured my family shuffling on their knees up and down the hilly gravel paths in the nearby South American village as locals ridiculed us from their porches. We begged for uncooked kernels of corn only to have them thrown at us in mockery.

A white two-seater prop plane with bold red stripes running along its sides pulled up at the mini-mart where my family and I were being held on the brink of a life of beggary. Flashing lights on the end of each wing shot red beams through the heavy night rain. The pilot and co-pilot both women in white flight suits, had come to refuel. I sensed an opportunity. If I could get the attention of one of the women, she could put a halt to the pending terror.

"Are you the pilot?" I asked the woman who had come inside while her counterpart fueled the plane.

"No, I'm a nurse with Swedish Hospital." She spoke so clearly, so officially.

Next thing I knew, I was looking down at the clouds from a window seat on a commercial jetliner, a Jack and Coke on the rocks with a small blue plastic straw in my right hand. Somehow, Angela had gotten the kids home. They were safe.

I felt relief beyond words. I wouldn't be knee-bound forever in a never-traveled South American village. Now I was going home.

"You got the kids home! How did you do that?!" I

exclaimed, looking at Angela the moment I awoke (for real). I turned to my mom.

"Why did you do that?" I asked. *What was she thinking when she told that guy to sew more lead into my pant legs?*

She had no idea what I was talking about.

I had been unconscious for nearly three weeks.

Even though I was no longer dreaming, I really couldn't move my legs. Looking toward the foot of my bed, I saw that they were wrapped in Velcro bandages that filled with air and deflated in rhythmic, mechanical cycles. I immediately tore off the bandages. After the nightmare of having my legs immobilized, I couldn't stand the feel of anything that constricted my lower limbs.

It was late spring 2014, nearly two years since the relapse of leukemia that had sent me to Swedish, where I had hallucinated in the ICU. Two years since Dr. Austin had issued the stark words that the leukemia would come back and that there would be no cure, which had left me counting down to the summer of the previous year as my end date. I'd exceeded it by a good twenty-one months (trust me—I counted the months), well beyond the nine-month median for expected survival, and was still alive. I had been living a full life—one of work, home, family, friends, travel, exercise. I felt great. And with each additional month of beating the odds, I felt that much better.

Then it hit.

Why am I so tired?

I was sitting in our living room on the white sectional, not understanding why I felt so fatigued. I was dizzy, out of breath, and exhausted. Suddenly and inexplicably, I dropped the mug of black tea I had been sipping.

Crap!

The piping-hot liquid landed on my lap as well as on the lovely white cushion next to me, creating a large brown stain.

If I hurry, maybe I can soak this up with a towel...

I stood and took three steps toward the kitchen, only to stumble.

What the...?

Determined to rescue the couch from disaster, as if it weren't already too late, I made my way to the drawer where we kept towels, using the kitchen island to steady myself. When I finally got back to the couch, I dropped to my knees so I could be at eye level with the stain while scrubbing it. Alas, it was too late. I had killed the couch. I tried to stand up but couldn't muster the strength, so I reached for the arm of the couch and used it to drag myself up onto the tea-soaked cushion, where I sat panting in a state of moderate alarm.

What's going on?

I reached into my pocket for my phone and called Angela. She answered on the second ring.

"I can't walk," I told her when she answered.

"What? What do you mean? You fell?"

"No. Not that. I mean I can't stand up. Something's wrong. I need you to come home and take me to the hospital."

I never asked to go to the hospital, so Angela knew something must be very wrong. She came home right away. When she arrived, we plotted the best way to get me to the car since I barely had the strength to stand.

"Should I call an ambulance?" she asked.

"No, I have an idea." I asked Angela to create a path from the couch to the car in the driveway using kitchen chairs, figuring I could make it from chair to chair. Fortunately, the stepping-stone tactic proved successful.

Minutes later, Angela pulled to the curb outside the emergency room at Swedish Issaquah, set the car in park, and walked through the sliding glass doors to ask for a wheelchair. An attendant came out right away and wheeled me inside, where I found myself sitting up in a hospital bed in one of the ER exam rooms.

"Do you mind if a student accompanies me to take notes?" asked the doctor as he entered.

I glanced at the young man with curly brown hair holding a clipboard and trailing the physician. *He seems innocuous enough.*

"Sure—no problem."

Dressed in wool slacks and a plaid dress shirt, the

physician walked to the side of my bed.

"Tell me what's going on."

I relayed the story and, after a bit of back and forth, the doctor told the nurse standing against the wall by the entryway to set me up for an x-ray. Soon after, a technician wheeled in a desk lamp the size of a bull, only the lamp had a large camera lens for a face. The technician draped a lead apron over my lap like a blanket, positioned the machine's lens so that it looked directly at my chest, stood back, and snapped a picture. And another. And another.

The room emptied, and I was left to stare in boredom at the flat-screen television on the wall, which was looping a video of exotic landscapes: desert, jungle, beach, mountains. Angela, meanwhile, sorted through the email from work that was blowing up her phone.

The doctor darted back into the room, his eyes wide as if he had witnessed a car crash. He stepped to the foot of the bed, looked directly into my eyes, and said ominously, "It's pneumonia. I'm so sorry."

Pneumonia? Why's he apologizing? People get pneumonia all the time. It's what my mom used to say would happen if I played outside in the rain too long. What's the big deal?

"I'm so sorry," he repeated, to Angela now. And then he hurried out of the room.

That was the last thing I heard, the last thing I recall seeing, before waking up nearly three weeks later, joyful and relieved that Angela had gotten the kids home safely from South America.

Angela: Why was the ER doctor apologizing to Walt and me? At the time I really had no idea, and was more focused on logistics than being alarmed. I assumed that it was bad but manageable. Once Walt was settled and gave me the signal that it was okay to leave, I headed home. I don't think I even accompanied him up to his room. He was his usual self-sufficient and resilient self.

I went back to the hospital the next day to check in on him, but didn't stay long. Instead I asked Walt's brother to go and hang out with him. Porter obliged and, before he left for the day, gave me a report: Walt was on oxygen but in good spirits and resting comfortably. I don't quite recall what I did that day, but my mom took the kids to her condo that night, leaving me alone at home where I snoozed on the couch in front of the TV with the dog.

A little past midnight my cellphone woke me.

"Mrs. Harp?"

No one called me by Walt's last name unless it was something official or serious. I was instantly alert.

"This is the charge nurse from floor six of Swedish Hospital in Issaquah," she told me. "I'm afraid your husband has taken a turn for the worse and we had to intubate him. That means he wasn't getting enough oxygen on his own, and he's now breathing through a tube in his trachea with the help of a machine. I'd recommend you come to the hospital right away."

Hanging up the phone, I moved into action mode. First, I called our friend Edie and woke her from a deep sleep. "What's the matter, Ange?" she asked groggily.

"The hospital just called and they had to intubate Walt. That's really bad, right? I should go up there."

I remember Edie trying to shield me a bit with her answer. "Yeah, that's not great. You should go. Do you need me to come with?" She sounded completely out of it, so I declined her generous offer. Once off the phone, however, I realized that the dog was going to need to be walked in the morning, and there was a strong possibility that I wouldn't be back in time. For help, I called another good friend— Amy. She was much more of a night owl and was one of my go-to friends like Edie in time of need. She was one of the first people I had called when Walt had been diagnosed. In addition to being one of the most capable and networked people that I knew, she had been a true friend through all of our trials, never hesitating to help.

When I arrived at her place to drop off our house key, she had already packed a bag and sleeping bag and insisted on making the half-hour ride up to Issaquah with me. Normally I wouldn't take her up on such an offer, but by this time I was sufficiently freaked out and said, "Yes, that would be great."

Amy caravanned to the hospital and upon arrival ran into the doctor on call as she exited Walt's room.

"Mrs. Harp, your husband's blood oxygen level was dipping below tolerable levels despite the oxygen we were giving him, so we had to intubate him. His lungs were compromised—filled with fluid. He's heavily sedated, but semiconscious. It's a critical situation."

My first question was whether he had sustained long-term oxygen deprivation to the brain and if there was a possibility of brain damage. Luckily the answer was no, but the moment Amy and I entered the room I saw he was in terrible shape.

Amy offered to stay the night, but at that point there was nothing more that she could do. Plus I knew that she had to go to work the next day.

"No, you should go. Thanks so much, though."

I sat vigil by Walt's bed. He wasn't yet in the ICU, so he wasn't getting one-on-one attention from the nursing stuff. I didn't feel comfortable leaving him alone. I didn't want him to wake up scared or to pull the tube out of his mouth. I kept trying to hold his hand to comfort him, which I later learned only served to stimulate and agitate him, keeping him from sleep.

It was one of the most terrifying nights of my life.

After finally getting some rest, I awoke to a nurse informing me that their lead pulmonary specialist, a Dr. Simons, would be coming soon. Her first words to me on arrival were something along the lines of: "Mrs. Harp, I'm so sorry, but your husband's situation is critical. Under different circumstances, I might even say his lungs are too far gone to save him. Fortunately, he's less than forty-five years old, and only one of his lungs has stopped functioning. And all of his other organs are intact. We have a chance to save him, but he needs to be transported to our facility in Seattle right away. Putting him in an ambulance at this point is a risk—there's no guarantee he'll get there alive. It could very well be touch and go."

Dr. Simons paused and searched my face for a response. I wasn't sure there was a question. Was she looking for my ok?

She spoke again.

"Let's do this, shall we?" she said, with such conviction that my panic evaporated. I saw that this woman knew what she was doing.

And frankly, there really wasn't any other option. If Walt was to survive, he had to get to Seattle.

"Yes, let's do it," I replied without having to think.

It was then that Walt started to regain consciousness. The fingers of his right hand, more pincers than digits, rose to his face and tried to take hold of the breathing tube.

"Stop trying to pull the tube out of your mouth!" I scolded. But he wouldn't.

Dr. Simons stepped in.

"Mr. Harp, this is Dr. Simons. I'm the pulmonary specialist taking care of you. You are in a very serious situation, and we need to transport you to our Seattle facility immediately. While we arrange for transport, though, I must strongly advise you NOT to pull the tube out of your mouth. I know it's uncomfortable and scary, but it's providing you the oxygen you need. Pulling it out will cause serious harm to your trachea, and I'll need to call in a crisis intervention team. No one wants that. You need to stay calm and let us take care of you to the best of our ability."

The doctor ordered me to be transferred by ambulance to Swedish First Hill in downtown Seattle, where a padded metal cocoon called a rotoprone would save my life.

On my arrival at First Hill, two technicians immediately lay me onto a thick plastic mat that covered a long, flat steel base. They strapped my body to it using aluminum-reinforced nylon belts, each strung with thick, stuffed, vinyl-covered pads the size of life jackets. One of the technicians affixed to my face a cushioned mask, not unlike what a boxer would wear in the training ring, and pinned it down to keep my head stationary. Once I was completely ensconced inside the medical sarcophagus, the same technician pressed a few of the buttons on a console at the end of the bed and rotated me 180 degrees so that I faced the floor.

There I hung midair for over two weeks.

Angela: At first, Walt was conscious in the rotoprone—and freaked out. When he saw his brother, who had driven downtown to meet us, Walt managed to communicate through sign language, "Get me out of here."

Running on very little sleep, I managed to muster enough energy to talk to the doctors, watch Walt get set up, call my boss, and spend time with the friends who had rallied to be there. At that point, I finally broke down and wept. Then I passed out on the couch.

For days, a Dr. James kept looping around the rotoprone, squinting his eyes and wringing his hands. "Mrs. Harp," he'd say, "This is very serious." Meanwhile, one of the physician assistants pulled me aside more than once to confide, "He may not make it. Are you ready?"

I stayed calm. "I think he'll be fine. Walt always pulls through." But what I really wanted to say was get the hell away from me.

Days passed. The staff would rotate Walt onto his back to see how long his lungs could sustain him without the help of gravity. He would last only a few minutes before his oxygenation dropped below 80 percent. They would then rotate him back.

I had allowed the hospital to place Walt in the rotoprone only after promising me that spending extended time unconscious wouldn't result in brain damage. I knew Walt wouldn't want to be kept alive if that were the case.

They promised me he'd be fine (and, thankfully, he is).

The machine was medieval yet sophisticated. Sure, it was a brutish cage. But it was nuanced enough to avoid tangling the tubes that fed into Walt while spinning him. It also allowed for staff to care for bedsores without changing Walt's position. And ice his face, which kept filling with fluid.

I spent a lot of time in the floor's family area, making calls to figure out whether and how I could go on leave from work. Asking friends and family for help managing the kids. Crying.

Our friend Edie, a physician, put together a collage made of pictures of Walt, me, and the kids. She posted it on the wall above the head of the rotoprone.

"It's not for Walt," she said. "It's for the staff. So they remember there's a human in that machine."[48]

Doctors would power-walk into the room, check diagnostics, and power out. Edie made it her business to call out, "That's the family sitting there," pointing to us.

I held Walt's hand. "Don't die on me," I said when no one else was around. 'You better come out of this.'

Everyone was on edge. Doctors, nurses. A patient in a rotoprone wasn't an everyday occurrence. There were a lot of variables and unknowns. The staff would include me in the huddle on morning rounds since I knew Walt's history better than anyone. We were all trying to hold it together.

Finally, I called Sharon. I thought, Walt may very well die here. His mom needs to know. She needs to have the opportunity to see him.

---

48   Edie (and remember, she was a physician) later told me she was terrified that this was the end—that Walt wasn't going to get out alive.

I'm so thankful she flew out. Not only were we able to trade shifts so that we could stay with Walt morning and night, but also she spoke to him nonstop. The whole rotoprone process was so inhuman. She made it human.

Nurses took shifts monitoring Walt's vitals around the clock. They would sit at one end of the rotoprone, making tiny, careful adjustments to Walt's position as needed. And they would speak to him as if he were awake.

"You don't like that, Walter? Let's move you a bit."

One nurse, afraid Walt might expire without her keeping watch, took double shifts. Nearly twenty-four hours straight.

Dr. James wouldn't stop with the circling and hand-wringing. Not only was Walt on the brink of drowning in his own lungs, but the hospital staff was still at a loss as to the exact nature of the infection at the root of the situation. The interminable wait for cultures to grow from the blood samples they extracted was excruciating. And it was only through the findings that the doctors could learn the culprit's identity.

Then one morning Dr. James's circling, mumbling, and hand-wringing stopped. Instead, he entered the room practically skipping. Smiling and relieved, he said he had identified the specific bacteria at the root of the pneumonia killing Walt. That meant he could back off of the broad-spectrum antibiotics he had been slamming Walt with and transition to narrow-spectrum ones. Not to sound overly violent, but think transition from carpet bombing to using a high-powered sniper rifle. Collateral damage drops in a big way.

Soon, Walt could maintain greater than 90 percent oxygenation when lying on his back. Eventually, the staff took him out of the rotoprone and laid him in a bed. He was still unconscious and a breathing tube remained in his throat, but he had made it out of the rotoprone.

Over the following days, hour after hour, the nurses kept asking Walt to lift one of his thumbs to show he was conscious. But it didn't happen. Sharon got to the point where she would literally lift one of his thumbs, again and again, saying "C'mon, Walt...You can do it." I worried Walt would lift a thumb when no one was there.

Talk of the giant unicorn balloon Walt's friends from work had sent him cascaded through the ward. Several people stopped by to visit it.

At last, the call came. Sharon was at the hospital. I was at home. It was 2 a.m.

"Mrs. Harp, I need you to phone me," the message said. It was a nurse whose name I didn't recognize.

Holy shit...he's dead! They don't contact the wife in the middle of the night if it's good news.

But it was.

When I called back, they said, "He's awake."

Kevin paid a visit while I was hanging on the spit.

"I didn't think you were going to make it out of there," he told me.

On seeing me walk into his office several weeks after the incident, my infection specialist looked at me with surprise and said, "We usually don't see people get out of the rotoprone."

That's haunting.

But somehow I did. I was one of the lucky ones.

Angela: Soon after Walt regained consciousness, one of the nurses brought him water to drink. As she put the straw in his mouth, Dr. James happened to walk in.

"Don't do that! He'll choke!" he yelled.

"He doesn't know Walt very well," whispered Edie, who was sitting next to me.

Walter, of course, finished the cup. This doesn't sound like an Olympic feat. But at the time it was.

My legs weren't the only part of my body I couldn't lift when I regained consciousness. I couldn't sit up, either. Even the simple act of trying to reach the buttons on the inside of the bed rails proved to be a Herculean challenge. I had very little motor control. In a mere seventeen days, I had lost virtually all my strength—a phenomenon that astounds me still to this day.

How could I have lost all my strength in such a short amount of time? What were the physics behind that? Was it because I was suspended in the air face down? Would this have happened had I been bedridden but not in the rotoprone?

Later, watching the television show *Game of Thrones*, I questioned how the Jaime Lannister character could still fight with full strength after being trapped motionless in a cage for a week. *That's so fake.* I could barely control my sphincter, let alone deliver a right cross.

I ended up soiling myself more than once in the days following the rotoprone and my subsequent return to consciousness. Oddly, I couldn't pee either. As a result, the staff inserted a clear plastic catheter into my penis so gravity could pull wastewater from my bladder. A nurse told me it would stay in until I could show that I was able to urinate on my own.

On the third day, a nurse pulled the catheter out. It felt like she was ripping a splintered chopstick out of my urethra. She checked on me every hour to see whether I had peed on my own by using an electronic gauge to measure the urine volume in my bladder.

She always found urine there. I couldn't pee.

"If you don't urinate, I'll put the catheter back in," she scolded.

Are you kidding me?

No joke—she was threatening me. *Finish your beans or you'll get a spanking!*

Trust me. The insertion of the catheter had been far worse than its removal (although the last time I had a catheter, the nurse mercifully introduced lidocaine gel into the equation—God bless modern medicine). There was absolutely no way I was letting her put that catheter back in.

Someone must have told her to lay off, because the nurse never came back.

"Hi, Daddy!" Sofia shouted as she bounced into the room the next day. "We have a surprise for you!"

"Shh!" hushed Luke, trailing Sofia. It had been almost three weeks since I had seen either of them.

"Surprise? What is it?" I asked, joyful.

"You'll find out!" Sofia replied. A second later, Hannah, our nanny, walked in, carrying a large canvas satchel with something rustling conspicuously inside.

She's lugging it with both hands. Must be heavy.

"You have a visitor!" said Hannah as she set the bag down next to me on the mattress. That's when I heard the sounds coming from inside. *Snort. Shuffle. Snort.*

A small black face with bulging eyes peeked over the top of the bag. It was Gracie, our baby, the pug we had recently rescued. Nose flat, fur shiny, expression pitiful.

"Gracie!" I exclaimed, joining in the merriment of the moment.

"The nurse let us bring her in," Hannah explained, "as long as we were stealthy about it, that is."

Love that nurse.

Gracie walked across my chest snorting, too excited by all the stimulation to settle down. Meanwhile Luke and Sofia played around in the room.

Here we go again. This should be a moment. I've been away from home. Haven't seen these guys forever. They even brought the dog. Engage! Show Hannah more appreciation for smuggling Gracie into the hospital!

But I was exhausted. *You want them to go already? They just got here!* I told myself.

Like I said, we don't live in a Hollywood movie where reunions necessarily bring tears of joy accompanied by a dramatic soundtrack. I loved my children, I loved our dog, I really appreciated Hannah's effort. But I was good for all of ten minutes at most.

Angela came by a few hours after the kids—and the dog—left. "Luke is very worried about you," she told me. "He's having trouble going to bed."

I had no idea he felt that way. On his visit, he had been the same old boisterous, funny, kinetic Luke. He had never flinched at the whole cancer thing—and at this point, there had been several years of it.

I guess he's old enough now that it's finally registering with him. What Angela told me added depth I didn't know existed to the relationship I had with my beautiful boy.

Angela: Walt is correct that this hospitalization hit Luke's radar on an entirely different level than previous stays. First, Walt forgot to tell you about the appendicitis. Happened just a week before the pneumonia. (Crazy, huh?) The kids had crawled into bed with us one morning, and when Walt tried to get up, his legs crumpled underneath him and he fell to the wood floor—hard. Turns out a severe infection had surfaced in his appendix (ugh). Seeing him fall, I started to panic and yelled for Luke to throw me my phone so I could call 911. I became completely focused on getting Walt to the hospital (which, by the way, he refused to do at first—the EMT basically had to force him to go). Unfortunately, what the kids saw was this: their father collapsing, their mother panicking, and the paramedics hustling their father into an ambulance and rushing him away.

How can that not affect your kids, particularly at ages seven and ten, old enough to comprehend calamity?

Once I got Walt to the hospital, my thoughts turned to how traumatizing the whole appendicitis scene might have been to the children, so I drove all the way back to their school to find and reassure them that Dad was ok. Fortunately, Walt managed to show up at Luke's baseball game two days later, right after surgery.

Once Walt was stable and out of the rotoprone, I debated the pros and cons of bringing the children to see their father even though he was still unconscious and intubated. I opted for "yes." They needed the reassurance of seeing him, even if the picture was a little scary.

Both were thrilled to see their father. Sofia moved on to engaging the nurse on duty in a high-spirited conversation around the mechanics of how Walt managed to poop and pee while lying down. Luke, at first, seemed fine, but I soon noticed him in the corner of the room looking out the window. I walked over and found him weeping silently.

"What's the matter, Lu?" I probed gently.

"It's really hard to see Daddy so sick like this," he replied.

Exhausted, I sighed and held him until he stopped crying. There was nothing else to do. He was right.

More broadly speaking, I had come to live in two very different worlds: one the ICU, one my home. I spent hours in the ICU each day monitoring Walt's oxygen levels, wondering how long he could stay on his back before having to be flipped over, worrying over whether the pressure of his face against the padding would prove too much for his eyeballs.

And when would he FINALLY wake up?!

Meanwhile, I had to manage the home front. Did I let the kids go camping with friends on Memorial Day as planned or did I send Luke to Eastern Washington for an end of season baseball tournament? Either way, how did I get them there? Who would watch them? Luckily, I had many friends who, as always, were willing to help. Babysitting, transporting, entertaining—our friends were very generous with their time and energy, which helped to keep Luke and Sofia's lives as normal and positive as possible despite the circumstances.

I ended up sending the kids on the camping trip over Memorial Day. While they were away, my best friend from middle school flew up from California to keep me company for a day, a much-needed break from stress and the hospital. The weather was gorgeous. We had a great time eating at my favorite dumpling place and getting full body massages. And we talked and talked and laughed. When evening came, though, and it was time for her to go home, I cried so hard that she offered to stay longer. I demurred. It didn't feel right keeping her away from her family.

Home I went. To a house so desolate it was chilling.

Luke's baseball continued in all its fanfare throughout this period and at times offered a good excuse for Sharon and me to escape the hospital. And do something fun. Outdoors!

Luke was a good player, but he had developed a fear of getting hit by the ball when at bat. Not surprising given that he seemed to get beaned by every pitcher. Regardless of what was going on with Walt, Luke hung in there, showing up with a smile, clowning around with friends, and playing with focus both in practice and in games. He's a strong kid that way. But also delicate, if that makes sense. Strong, outgoing, athletic, competitive, energetic, funny, social—yet fragile. Perhaps as many young boys are.

The last game of the season, the one that would determine whether Luke's team would go to the playoffs, was a heartbreaker. Bottom of the ninth, bases loaded with two outs, down by two, and Luke was up at bat. Don't think that just because he was ten years old he didn't feel pressure. A _LOT_ of it. I sat in the stands right behind the plate and could tell he was feeling tentative.

Now, like I said, Luke was a good player. At the time, though, he had hit a bit of a slump. So I probably shouldn't have been overly surprised when I overheard another parent sigh, "Oh no. Not Luke." My faced flushed. This mama bear was ready to stand on her hind feet and swipe. But I held off, even though I wanted to curse the person out.

"You have no idea what he's going through, jerk-off..."

Luke, like his father, came through. After three balls and a strike, he caught a piece of the ball and popped it up toward second base. The parents cheered as we all watched the ball arc through the air—only to be caught by the shortstop. Game over.

I watched Luke's shoulders drop. He turned and walked back to the dugout, where he buried his face in his hands. The coach, who knew what we were going through, grabbed him—literally picked him up—and reassured him that Luke had done an awesome job.

He was right, but Luke wasn't able to hear the feedback.

I shuttled Luke to the car. He continued to cry. I tried to comfort him with motherly words of wisdom. I told him how proud I *was of him for swinging the bat despite being scared. I was sincere, but my mothering was of little use in the moment. He looked at me from the backseat and said very poignantly, "Mom, it's not the game. I feel like I will never be happy again."*

There was little I could do at that point to make him feel otherwise, so I grabbed the phone and called Walt, who miraculously picked up. I have no idea what was said. I was just glad that Luke's father was at least alive and conscious and able to be of some support.

Angela was sitting next to me in the hospital room, typing away at her email as I dozed, when a young woman bounded into the room and shout-troduced herself.

"I'm Patricia!" she beamed as she removed the bike helmet from her head, revealing a healthy mop of curly red hair. "Your physical therapist!"

Over the next few days, Patricia helped me to sit up in bed and do light arm movements. She even got me to stand with the aid of a nurse, but abandoned the effort after I defecated the moment I reached my feet.

"Well, I guess we're not ready for that today," Patricia said kindly.

I felt ashamed at the smell and sad I had caused the party to end.

"You're going to want to go to the acute rehabilitation

program at Swedish Cherry Hill," Patricia told me the next day. "It's by far the best. Best staff, best equipment—everything. That's how you'll get back on your feet the fastest. Trust me—that's where you want to go."

Sounds awesome. Count me in.

"Dr. Teal is going to take a look at you later today to decide if you're in good enough condition to go there. It's a very intense program. Hours of rehab every day. It takes a *lot* of stamina."

That doesn't bother me.

Dr. Teal did come by later that day. As he leafed through a manila folder containing some of my medical records, he asked me questions about how I was feeling. He didn't submit me to any physical tests, just eyed me from where he stood.

Moments later, Dr. Teal dashed my newfound dreams of Ivy League rehab and decided not to recommend me for Cherry Hill.

"I don't think you'll be set up for success there, Walt," Dr. Teal explained. "You need more time to recover. You need more strength. The program at Cherry Hill is strenuous. If I send you there, I'll be setting you up for failure. It'll prove overwhelming."

An hour later, a care coordinator entered the room with a clipboard. "Dr. Teal feels it's best if we start you in a nursing home for a while before we get you to Cherry Hill."

Although I was still physically weak, my head had cleared. The words "nursing home" caught my attention.

Are you kidding me?

"This is a list of facilities you can choose from," the coordinator said, handing the clipboard to Angela.

"What about Aljoya on Mercer Island?" Angela queried, referring to a high-end assisted living facility located near our home.

"They don't take rehab patients there, but there are plenty of good ones on the list that do."

The coordinator walked out, leaving us to browse the menu of senior care facilities even though I was only forty-three years old. Assisted living facilities are legitimate environments for people who, even though they aren't seniors, need to rest and regain strength. I didn't know that at the time, and even if I did, I still would have been horrified at the thought of having to go to one. Probably not the most politically correct or educated thing to say, but it's true. The images that popped into my mind were not appealing.

Angela: Walt's mom was beside herself. She didn't want to "see my son in diapers!" as she said to me when I told her.

We all love and respect Walt's mom, but when Sharon gets fixated on something, it can take a lot of effort to talk her off her ledge, which I tried to do; I felt we didn't have enough information to be sure Walt should be going to a nursing home. But it wasn't time to panic. I told Walt that he had always defied expectations and that I felt this time would be no different. Perhaps I was deluding myself, but somehow I believed he'd be fine.

"I want another assessment," I stated flatly when the care coordinator returned. "And I want Patricia here. I am *not* going to a nursing home. I am *plenty* ready for Cherry Hill."

The coordinator stared at me, not sure what to say. She left the room without a word. A physician's assistant took her place.

"He doesn't have the strength," she scoffed to Angela. "Look at him."

Angela called Patricia in and with her help, I stood and walked all the way across the room to the sink and back. I did it again. And again. I even brushed my teeth. There was no fucking way I was going to a nursing home (apologies for the crassness, but I was terrified at the prospect). *I was going to Cherry Hill.*

"I don't mean to be mushy, but you are exactly the reason I went into physical therapy," Patricia said with tears in her eyes as she helped me lie back in bed.

She was happy to have made a difference. And she had. A big one.

Dr. Teal visited me again. After Patricia passionately pleaded my case and explained what had happened, he left to reconsider his decision. When he returned, he told Angela and me that he was going to recommend Cherry Hill.

CHERRY HILL

"I'm sorry, Walt. We're not going to be able to do anything today," Michael, one of the physical therapists assigned to me, said in a matter-of-fact yet sympathetic tone. Even though I had made it to Cherry Hill, the staff there wouldn't let me begin rehabilitation. My blood pressure was too low and even standing left me wobbly. I had to lie there in a stupid bed frustrated that I couldn't move forward.

What am I supposed to do to keep myself occupied? Maybe Dr. Teal was right. Maybe it's too soon to be here.

Michael saved me.

"Screw it," he said the next day, even though my blood pressure continued to register low and I felt dizzy when standing. "We're not going to get anywhere if we leave you in bed, right?"

Thus began rehab. Afternoons with Michael, mornings with one of two female therapists who alternated shifts with each other.

At first, Michael would wheel me to the exercise room since there was no way I could walk the football-field distance. Even with the help of a walker, I could only make it a few steps before having to sit. I didn't have the strength, stamina, or stability.

Over the course of a few days, things changed. Yard by yard, I shuffled across longer and longer sections of the hallways, at first with the walker, then, more adventurously, with the cane. Sofia and Luke would skip backwards in front of me, calling out words of encouragement. "Come on, Dad!" Angela would trail me with a wheelchair to use as a portable rest stop.

Meanwhile, the morning therapists, who started out conservative, soon gave me more and more freedom. Whereas at first I wasn't allowed to go to the bathroom alone (not that I could have physically done so even if I tried!), after a few days, they let me shower and brush my teeth by myself. With the door closed. Freedom!

I progressed so rapidly that the morning therapists began to feel stumped as to what to do with me. First, they gave me arm exercises, using weight machines while sitting. In the following days, I moved to playing "soccer" in the mat room, folding clothes, and bowling with the Nintendo Wii, a game in which I bested my friend Jeff, a more agile athlete than I, who had kindly broken away from work to pay me a visit at Cherry Hill.

Still, despite the progress, one of the nurses on rotation couldn't stop with the criticism: I stood too quickly. I didn't pee enough. I sat too quickly.

"We don't like it when patients plop like that."

She and I argued over the compression stockings I was told to wear on my legs to improve blood pressure. After my nightmares in the rotoprone, I still couldn't stand the feel of anything that restricted my legs. Five minutes after she put them on me, I rolled them off, no small feat given how tight those suckers were and what little strength and stamina I had.

When she checked on me I told her "I don't need them," causing her eyebrows to furrow.

"Dr. Teal ordered them. You need to do as he says."

"Go ask him again. Tell him I'm not going to wear those things."

"We'll see about that."

The nurse stormed out. She never mentioned the nylons again. Dr. Teal told her I didn't have to wear them.

Then, there was the afternoon when I was in the hallway with Michael alternating between walking upright and taking rests in a wheelchair. At one point, Michael forgot to set the brakes when it was time for me to sit. He turned his head just long enough for me to end up pushing the wheelchair away with my butt as I tried to lower myself onto the seat. Instead, I fell to the laminate floor. More accurately, I ended up plopping to the ground ever so lightly onto my padded rear. No harm done, but the staff reacted in accordance with the protocol they were required to follow. Michael, suddenly serious, ordered me to stay where I was, on the floor. Another nurse rushed over with a cart and began interrogating me about the "incident" as she typed my answers into a computer.

I get the need for protocol, but isn't this a little over the top? With all the alarm and bustle, you would have thought a plane had crashed.

The same nurse who had interrogated me as I sat on the floor in the hallway later came to my room to tell me that from then on, I was to wear a safety belt while in bed.

I was already miserable enough. There was no way I was going to be strapped to my bed. "I'm not going to do that."

The nurse went to get the floor supervisor, who surprised me by being calm, rational, and understanding (I had expected a strict rule-master).

"It was an accident," I explained. "I wasn't trying to stand up on my own. I wasn't breaking the rules. I don't need to be restrained. Michael didn't set the brakes on the wheelchair. I fell back. That's all."

I guess I was throwing Michael under the bus a bit. But, really, I was stating the facts, not trying to divert blame. I couched the statement by describing how awesome Michael was (which he truly was).

"I see. It was an accident," the supervisor said empathetically. She mulled silently over what I had told her. "Well...we can forgo the safety belt, but I think it would be good for all of us if we could set an alarm on your wheelchair. At least for a day." The wheelchair alarm would go off should I try to stand up. An annoying prospect, but she was offering a reasonable compromise, so I took it. *Wheelchair alarm for twenty-four hours—I'll deal.*

At the staff meeting on Friday, less than a week from the day of my admittance to the acute rehab program at Cherry Hill, Michael and my morning therapists made the case for my release. From their perspective, I now met the key criteria: I was in a good-enough condition that I could care for myself at home. I could walk a long hallway (with a cane or walker), bathe myself, feed myself, and get up from the floor if I fell.

I was granted discharge.

Thank God it wasn't Nurse Critical in there speaking on my behalf. I'd be in here forever!

The kind folks at Cherry Hill gifted me a shiny new aluminum walker, finished in eggplant purple and complete with padded seat, as well as a wooden cane to take home. The plan? Live on the first floor until I could garner the strength to climb the stairs to the master bedroom on the second.

Well, that was the plan until I actually walked through the front door of the house.

OK...Michael had me walk stairs as part of my therapy. Only three stairs—up three, down three—but he had me walk stairs nonetheless. I might be able to make it up if I rest on the landing between the first and second rises.

I asked my mother to duct tape a kitchen chair to the landing, creating a recovery stop between the rises. And it worked. I made it upstairs. Now I could live on both floors.

The great outdoors, though, was a completely different story. The first time I went outside, I didn't make it much beyond the driveway.

"Let's turn around here," I said to my mother, who had kindly accompanied me on this first of many walks. With the help of the purple walker, I had managed to make it to the next-door neighbor's mailbox. Not exactly a hike. Over the ensuing couple of weeks, though, my adventures grew in distance from a few yards to half a mile (two loops around the neighborhood). I swapped out the walker for the more challenging cane. Eventually I stopped using assistive devices altogether. I even brought our pug Gracie with me for a walk, a move perhaps too ambitious as I ended up in the emergency room after Gracie crossed in front of me unexpectedly and I tripped on her leash. I had no arm strength to break the fall, so I hit the asphalt with my face, opening a gash over my left eye. I fell in that exact same position two more times over the ensuing days, once at a supermarket and another time on our patio. Each time I ended up back in the ER for stitches over the same eye!

The *Pneumocystis jiroveci* pneumonia (PCP) that had landed me in the rotoprone is particularly virulent for those whose immune systems are compromised, as is the case with cancer patients undergoing chemotherapy. My case had come out of nowhere. Literally. I never saw it coming. It never even occurred to me as a possibility.

I am now careful to take antibacterial medicine every day on top of the vaccine I received with the hope of warding off any future recurrence of pneumonia. It's not really the risk of death I'm concerned about—I never want to lose all my strength like that again. That was not a fun hole to have to climb out of.

I just want my family and my work. That's all. Simple wants.

And, ok, I want the ability to move, too. Physical activity enlivens me, even if it's just a loop around the block with a purple aluminum walker.

After I had regained the ability to ambulate, I went in for physical therapy per the hospital's orders. Now, I have enormous appreciation for physical therapy. But in this case, it wasn't enough. Or at least I didn't have the patience to give it a chance. I quit after the first session.

This is useless. I'm spending more time on my back stretching than I am doing anything that resembles strength building.

Of course, it didn't help that, as goodhearted as the therapist was, he wouldn't stop with the bad jokes. It was exhausting. So, a few weeks later, back at work in downtown Seattle, I joined a Gold's Gym, located around the corner from my office, and hired a trainer, something else I had never done before—trainers aren't cheap. I wanted my strength back. And muscle mass. Not for vanity, although I guess that always comes into play, but to be *functional* again.

On my first day, I was introduced to Tiffany, my new strength trainer. Tiny, sweet in temperament, and barely out of college, she would never be picked out of a lineup as a weight coach. But she was one. And as friendly as her disposition was, she was an ass-kicker underneath.

"So...what are you looking to do? Build muscle mass? Gain strength?" Tiffany asked.

"All of that. I spent a month in the hospital and lost everything."

Tiffany smiled and without blinking led me to the first station in a forty-five-minute custom circuit. At the end of that, Tiffany had me do push-ups.

"Three...four...five...six..." Embarrassed, I fell to the floor, having gone as far as I could, a sad performance that made Tiffany laugh.

"Don't worry. You'll get there," she assured me.

I worked out every day—twice a week with Tiffany and the rest of the time by myself, repeating or riffing on what she had taught me. Three weeks after my first training session, I fell to the marble floor at the food court across the street from my office. This time, though, I caught myself with my arms before hitting the floor with my face. Saved by a matter of centimeters.

Yes!

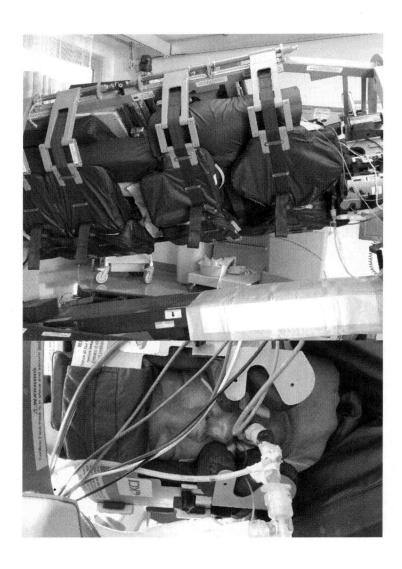

Above: The rotoprone (May 2013). I still can't believe that's me in there. Thank God
I was unconscious.

Below: A padded face mask protects me from damage due to gravitational
pull (May 2013).

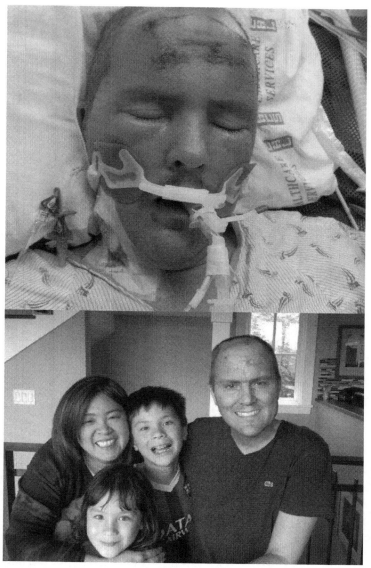

Above: Finally free of the rotoprone yet still unconscious for several days and not breathing on my own (June 2013).

Below: Home! (June 2013). Note the scar tissue from the face mask—as if I needed more scars.

TINY NINJAS, SEPTEMBER 2014

For my birthday, some good friends gave me a homemade gift, a bike helmet spray-painted in gold and covered with stickers and glitter along with the words 'Captain Indestructible.' I can't really take the credit for surviving, but it felt good to be Captain Indestructible nonetheless. I was now two years out from my last relapse and well past the median life expectancy of nine months I had been told to expect. I was also well into my first stage of physical recovery from the rotoprone.

A month later, Dr. Austin told me during one of my monthly visits to her office for blood monitoring, an ongoing effort to spot relapse early, that "There's a clinical trial at the SCCA for treatment of leukemia—ALL, in fact— that I want you to check out."

I'm completely bucking the odds. Who knows? Maybe this'll keep up…maybe the leukemia will never come back. I'm twenty-four months out!

"I've already made arrangements with a Dr. Mallory. He's running the CAR T trial," Dr. Austin continued. "You need to contact him for an appointment."

CAR T-cell therapy—CAR T, as it's called—is part of the current wave of innovation in immunotherapy, utilizing a patient's own immune system to fight cancer.[49]

---

49   It's an innovation today as I write this. Five to ten years from now, however, it will probably be standard treatment and we will marvel at the antiquated methods previously used to treat cancer. One day, our children's children will read about chemotherapy in history books, as we read about the telegraph.

Specialists harvest a patient's T cells, a subset of white blood cells, and genetically modify them so that when they are later reintroduced into the patient's blood system, the T cells recognize and kill tumorous cells.[50] In the case of leukemia, these bionic micro-ninjas kill leukemic blasts.

"You believe they'll accept me into the trial?" I asked Dr. Austin. "You and I both know my history is pretty darn unique. Do you think they'll be ok with the fact that I've had leukemia in my spinal fluid?"

"We'll find out."

A week later, Angela and I sat across from Dr. Mallory at a long white table in a warmly lit conference room on the sixth floor of the SCCA. Cars sped by on an interstate bridge rising outside the window. With salt-and-pepper hair parted to the side and a kind, sober face, Dr. Mallory described in a direct and concise manner the approach his small team was taking.

"The treatment is new—very new," he explained, "but the results show great promise. Of the several dozen patients treated so far, all of whom suffered from leukemia, over 90 percent have achieved remission and remain alive."

These people had run out of options. CAR T offered the last hope. And so far, it was working.

---

50   The US National Cancer Institute explains how CAR T therapy works: "After collection, the T cells are genetically engineered to produce special receptors on their surface called chimeric antigen receptors (CARs). CARs are proteins that allow the T cells to recognize a specific protein (antigen) on tumor cells."

As Dr. Mallory continued to hold forth, I couldn't help but question whether I'd qualify. The anticipation made me anxious.

I'm not going to get in. They've only accepted a handful of people, and I've had too many relapses, not to mention leukemia in my cerebrospinal spinal fluid. I'm sure that's a disqualifier.

I had to force myself to concentrate and ignore the negative internal voices.

The volume of Dr. Mallory's voice dropped as he reached the end of his overview. He paused for what seemed like forever, the muffled noise of the interstate the only sound in the room.

Finally, he spoke. "I think you would be a great candidate for the trial," he said looking at both Angela and me.

My heart jumped. I was ecstatic.

"That's wonderful!" Angela exclaimed.

He didn't say I would qualify. He said I would be a great candidate!

That felt good. Like I had won a sports championship.

A few weeks later, technicians at the SCCA harvested T cells using a centrifuge-like machine that isolated the cells from other components in my blood. The search for suitable veins was difficult, but the procedure itself was easy, requiring little more than spending a couple of hours in a recliner. Once the technicians had collected a critical mass of T cells, they put them in frozen storage for future use, should I come to need them. A good thing, given that the blasts returned to my cerebrospinal fluid a few months later.

At least it's not in my marrow.

Dr. Austin contacted Dr. Mallory to see if we could move ahead with the CAR T therapy.

"The treatment will only work if the blasts are in his blood," he told her. And since the blasts weren't in my blood—they were only in my spinal fluid—I went back to chemo. Methotrexate, to be exact. I received six injections over six days into the CSF through the Ommaya reservoir, which (thankfully) was still dug into my head like a spider in the sand. The chemo was outpatient; I was on and off the table in Dr. Austin's office within minutes each time. I experienced no side effects. And the leukemia disappeared from the CSF, at least enough so that tests couldn't pick it up.

By this time, I had almost come to take for granted that chemo would put me in remission, although I knew that at some point my luck would run out. The blasts would develop resistance, and I'd be left with no recourse. That's what happens. That's one of the reasons people die from leukemia.

In late May of 2015, the cancer returned. Again, it was in the spinal fluid. By this time, however, Dr. Mallory and his team had learned enough about the workings of CAR T to conclude that CAR T *could* work despite the fact that the blasts were only in the CSF. The primary risk: there might not be enough leukemic cells present in the CSF to incite the T cells to attack. The T cells don't care so much when they come across a couple of suspicious thugs here and there. They respond to mass violence.

CAR T was but two years old, and only 250 people in the world had been treated with it.

"It remains very new—still very experimental," explained Dr. Tuttle, Dr. Mallory's research partner. "You'll be the first patient to be treated with leukemia present only in the CSF. Everyone else has had it in their marrow. We're not a hundred percent sure what will happen."

I didn't care in the slightest. I was excited to have the opportunity.

"The most common side effects from the therapy are high fever and delirium from "cytokine storm," which means the T cells become overactive. Symptoms usually arise within two to five days after infusion. Patients generally spend no more than a week in the hospital." Dr. Tuttle paused. "Only one patient has died from treatment."

OK. Unsettling but not terrifying.

Two weeks later, I began a series of tests at the SCCA, followed by three days of outpatient chemo, including one stint of twelve hours in the recliner. Meanwhile, the trial team thawed my frozen T cells and transformed them bio-magically into microscopic assassins armed with antigen detectors that incited them to identify and kill blasts. I found myself back in one of the infusion therapy rooms at the SCCA with an IV in my arm. A technician hung the bag of precious, genetically modified T cells from a pole and turned on the pump to allow the life-saving material to enter my veins.

Angela: As I sat near Walt, the room felt isolating, almost lonely. Despite all the love from family and friends, it was ultimately just the two of us. As had been the case all along, were Walt to die, it would be the kids and me who would suffer most.

"Smile," I said as I took Angela's picture with my phone.

Despite everything that was at stake, the occasion itself was a nonevent. As with the stem cell transplant, the procedure was not much different from receiving blood. That was it.

At least, that was it for a few days.

CYTOKINE STORM

"Walter, I need you to focus. This is *very* important!" shouted the man shining a bright beam into my eyes.

Angela: Everyone was keyed up, including the physician assistant doing the interrogation. He was almost in a panic, time and again telling me that he had served in Iraq and was used to being under attack.

The situation did feel a bit like a gunfight.

This was new. It wasn't a tried-and-true stem cell transplant. People knew what to expect from that. With CAR T, they didn't. That's what put them on edge.

I was standing on the laminate floor of a room that was completely dark save for the penlight.

"What year is it?" he demanded.

I answered him, only marginally conscious. "2015."

"Who is the president?"

Pause.

"Who is the president, Walter?"

"Obama."

"*Where* are you?"

Silence.

When I regained a degree of clarity two days later, I thought the stretch of brick buildings and greenery outside the window could be Europe. I knew it wasn't (I wasn't *that* confused), but I hadn't yet come to realize where I was. Another two days went by before I pieced together that I was in a room on the bone marrow transplant ward of the University of Washington Medical Center, exactly where my transplant had taken place six years ago.

I can't believe I'm here. This is surreal. Yet it all felt so familiar, sentimental even. Taking walks around the

A-shaped hallway brought me back in time as I passed landmarks like the unused exercise bike, the view of the parking lot by the football stadium, and, of course, the ward's ICU, which was strangely empty.

Where are the patients with CPAP masks on their faces?

It took a while for my normal mental acuity to return, something the researchers were interested in knowing more about since this side effect was common to CAR T-cell therapy but not well documented. Angela suggested that they test my mental fitness by having me play Wordament on my phone, a game like Boggle only with a timer. Before the therapy, I was reasonably adept at it. I could maintain face when playing with friends. In the test...? I scored half my average.

Fuck.

After six days, I was discharged from the hospital, but not before having a job interview by phone in my room. The start-up where I worked had started to burn cash, so to stay solvent, the company ended up having to cut both staff and executive leadership, myself included. A few weeks earlier, the then-CEO, whom I still like and respect, had told me my position was being eliminated— he could no longer afford me. This was the very day Dr. Austin informed me that the leukemia had returned to my cerebrospinal fluid.

I would say that when it rains it pours, but neither the layoff nor the relapse came as a surprise. It was just a bit of life's color that the two came hand in hand. And it served as a good reminder that cancer doesn't happen in a vacuum. Life doesn't hold still to make way for the illness. You still have to manage day-to-day reality, which includes earning a paycheck.

Over the following days and weeks, tests of my blood, bone marrow, and spinal fluid showed that the CAR T therapy had worked. I was in complete remission. The blasts were gone yet again. And it happened so easily it was almost hard not to take the miracle for granted. *Take two aspirin and the cancer will be gone in the morning.*

Probably the only side effect of CAR T that really bothered me was the fatigue. I felt extremely lethargic for almost a month after the T-cell infusion. Very frustrating. I wanted my life back, but I had no energy. I probably could have been more patient, but the weariness persisted long enough that I grew scared that I'd be stuck that way, that fatigue would be the new normal. Angela and I even went so far as to ask SCCA staff to fill out forms to support an application for long-term disability, which we almost filed.

The CEO of the start-up kept me on the payroll for a couple of months to close things out, so I returned to work. Except for the fact that I still often can't recall names of celebrities, which could be due to age and not the CAR T, my cognitive agility ultimately returned. The fatigue subsided. My energy came back.

Not a scratch from the CAR T.

Magic.

Poof.

Angela: When they called me to explain they had to pull back on the treatment—that they had to give Walt steroids to counteract the T-cell overactivity (the cytokine storm)—that was a sobering moment. Up until that point, I had been unusually calm about the whole thing. Perhaps numb, just as I was when walking up the West Side Highway after watching people jump from the top of the Twin Towers on 9/11 to escape the burning jet fuel. I realized that the treatment might send him into a vegetative state. And I was torn. Continue the treatment, our last hope, or pull back?

Sitting in front of the TV at home with the lights off, Luke, now eleven, surprised me when he asked, "What are we going to do if Daddy doesn't make it?"

I didn't know how to answer and instead wept silently next to him, the darkness masking my tears. I dodged the question to buy time. "The doctors are doing everything they can to make sure that he's okay."

Luke slept in my bed that night. In the morning I shook him awake. "Luke, if Daddy dies, the three of us will take care of each other," I told him.

Luke's response? "What? I don't want to talk about that anymore." He was already over it.

The resilience of children.

When Walt regained his senses, he went back to being...well...Walt. His primary concern? A deal with Twitter he was brokering for the start-up where he worked.

I never doubted that the therapy would be successful. I had faith. And the fact that there was no known litany of torturous side effects, as there was with stem cell transplants, put my mind at ease. It was watching him suffer that I couldn't stand.

The CAR T cells—genetically engineered to find and kill lymphocytic blasts—have arrived (July 2015).

KEEP YOU AROUND

In the end, the words Dr. Getzen spoke to me the night she held my hands in the exam room at the SCCA and told me I had relapsed, the night when I bumped into the back of a stranger's Honda, rang true: There's always the possibility that new life-saving treatments will arise to address whatever disease is riding on your back and thus, as Dr. Getzen said, "Keep you around for your children."

No guarantees, but it can happen. It has for me (at least so far). Why not for you or for someone you cherish? It's not self-deluding to hold onto hope amid the fear and despair. Yes, it's scary, jarring, and horrible to have to plan for the worst—an awful predicament. But don't *rule out* at least a little hope. There's no reason to.

I afford myself a reasonable level of practical optimism, despite the fact that I'm a stark realist who never counts a deal done until the contract is signed. And mine isn't signed—just extended. Meanwhile, I wake up each morning, drink (too much) coffee, make lunches for Luke and Sofia, and start the day again, knowing that our world is fragile and temporary, yet permitting myself to live in the present.

VIGILANCE

I felt strangely off-balance at yoga last week. Back home, I was too woozy to sit upright at my desk, so I spent a good portion of the afternoon sleeping on the teal couch in the study. The next day I thought my balance had returned, yet, once again, I found myself teetering during yoga, unable to hold even the most basic positions. Something was off. And the lack of balance made me think of the time I couldn't get up from the couch after spilling my cup of tea...the time when Angela took me to the ER and I ended up in the rotoprone.

I took myself to Swedish for a chest x-ray.

Nothing. All good. But still concerned, I went to Dr. Austin's office to get my blood checked.

Maybe it's the leukemia.

When my phone rang the next morning and I saw that the screen said "Dr. Austin," I took a breath and girded myself. She had the results.

Rather than let the phone ring forever or go to voicemail, I ripped the Band-Aid off and answered on the second ring.

"Hello?"

"Hi, Walt. It's Marion."

I held my breath. "Yes?"

"Dr. Austin wanted me to call you."

Pause.

"The results came in and your blood and CSF tests are clean," she sang.

PART IV:
THE CARNIVAL CONTINUES

DARN IT, DECEMBER 2015

I wasn't planning on writing a Part IV. I thought I'd be able to end the story with Marion's call that day. But no...

A few months passed, and then shortly after Thanksgiving last year the graft in my left leg collapsed again. Surprising, given that it had been well over five years since the last time the graft had failed and Dr. Chao thought we might have to amputate. The grafts had become stable enough that I only needed to check in with Dr. Hills semiannually. I seldom thought about the durability of the bypasses. Dr. Hills had told me it was uncertain how long the grafts would last since most people who get femoral bypasses are elderly and end up passing away before the grafts give out. There isn't a lot of data on long-term structural integrity.

The bypasses probably won't last. Worst case? They'll amputate my legs below the knees and I'll get prostheses. I'll request carbon legs so I can run again.

Still, the collapse was a downer. Four days of bed rest. Not allowed to move. Had to lie on my back in the ICU and stay completely still because a catheter ran through the artery that went from my groin to my feet. A wrong twist or turn would have punctured the artery.

In the end, the doctors resurrected the bypass but told me I couldn't do yoga again for a while. I hated having to give up a piece of my life yet again.

No one knows why the graft closed. It wasn't scar tissue. Either way, I've been put on blood thinners. I take oral pills now, but for a few weeks I had to stab myself with a needle twice a day, bruising as easily as an overripe peach.

Fortunately, this all happened the week *before* my first day back at Microsoft. It would have been a crappy way to kick things off otherwise.

RELENTLESS, AUGUST 2016

Dr. Augtin left a voice message for me last week.

"Hey, Walt. I hate to leave this over the phone, but I'm in the San Juan Islands on vacation without cell coverage. And I don't want you to be left wondering about the results of last week's Ommaya draw.

"I, uh...well...it's me calling you, so I'm sure you know I don't have great news to share.

"The test on your CSF showed positive for blasts.

"I'm so sorry to have to tell you this.

"There aren't many, so that's good news. But they're there.

"I have you scheduled to come in on Monday for a biopsy so we can see whether there are blasts in your marrow, too. And I want to confirm their presence in the CSF.

Fortunate enough to steal a final splash of summer in Chelan, WA, despite the leukemia's return (September 2016).

"I've already spoken with Dr. Tuttle. We're probably going to have you go back in for the CAR T again. You should be hearing from his office shortly.

"I'm going to have phone coverage for the next twenty minutes. If you get this, please call.

"Listen, we've been through this before. We'll just make it happen like we always have."

Dr. Austin's words were warm and caring, yet her voice was thin and distant, as if traveling through a cotton string connecting two empty soup cans between the San Juan Islands and my kitchen. The significance of what she said registered, yet her voice was so far away it felt as if it weren't quite real. Nevertheless, the room where I sat began to rotate as the floor started to turn on its side. The sensation only lasted for a moment. I was working from home that day and couldn't afford to lose focus on the time-bound tasks I needed to finish. As usual, I compartmentalized the news, though I did seize up for just a moment in the hallway. I dry-heaved a single sob.

New term: cry-heave.

Later, I grieved for this book. Which may sound superficial, but I had come to believe my story would help others dealing with cancer. There went my happy ending. No more victory lap.

It was supposed to be a story of survival. One of hope. Now what is it? It's a downer. A buzz-kill. My book isn't going to comfort anyone with cancer. Quite the opposite—it'll scare them.

Then I recalled early on, way back in 2009, reading books about people enduring ongoing, sometimes terminal illness, such as *Always Looking Up* by Michael J. Fox and *Strong at the Broken Places* by Richard M. Cohen. Those stories comforted me. Call it misery loves company, call it what you will, I found solace in them. Maybe others will find solace in my book. A friend who, like them, endures.

Part of me wants to return to storytelling mode. Get back into narrative. Follow the writer's rule of show, not tell. But I think I need to wrap this up. Who knows when and how the narrative will end? Heck, the Star Wars anthology keeps going and going. Let's just stop here at the *Empire Strikes Back* and net things out.

First, I'm not panicked or traumatized by the news. Angela isn't either, although she cried when I told her about Dr. Austin's voicemail. We cancelled the dinner we had planned to celebrate our wedding anniversary that evening (leukemia is truly inconsiderate). Instead we stayed home, ordered pizza, and watched HGTV, still our go-to comfort food for the mind. Then we rallied. Angela scheduled a couples' massage for the next night, which I accidentally slept through after a long day at work and little rest the night before.

This last punch didn't knock us out. We didn't even hit the canvas. Had I heard that I needed another transplant, things might be different. That's a far tougher prospect than a mere week of fever and mild delirium in the hospital, which I expect will once again follow the T-cell infusion scheduled to happen next week. Sure, nothing's guaranteed. Something could go wrong, but (knock on wood) chances are it won't. I'll get another extension on my lease. And then maybe another one after that. And after that. Or not. Either way, my family and I will cross the next bridge when we arrive at it.

The kids don't seem fazed by the news, but then again, they're not always vocal about their feelings. Except maybe with Angela. I will try to draw it out of them, though there may be little to draw out. They're still young. Angela and I aren't playing out any drama in front of them. Life proceeds apace. In fact, I took the family back to Lake Chelan last weekend—a spur-of-the-moment decision. Talk about coming full circle. Looking back as I write this, I see I couldn't have planned such a metaphorical "return" if I'd tried.

I organized the trip to Chelan in part because of the leukemia and the pending treatment and ever-present risk of death or disability, which immediately brings into focus the things that are most important: the people I love and who love me. But also summer was about to end, and I needed one last taste, leukemia or no, which Chelan serves up par excellence. We even got out on the jet skis again. Really, really, really fast ones! (Perhaps NASA was behind the design?) Unlike when she was five, Sofia, now nine, demurred on the offer to drive. Luke, though, now twelve, jumped at the chance. The three of us rode together:

Luke, Sofia, and me. Laughing and laughing as I tried not to dump the kids off the back by going too fast over the choppy water. Even Angela joined in the fun, hugging me tight with one arm as we shot across the lake.

I couldn't help but reflect on how adrenaline and joy erase all concern.

Friends who read early drafts of the book told me, "Add more emotion! Tell me what you were thinking!" I've done my best to do that, but I've realized that part of the story is in fact the true-to-life *lack* of emotion at times. Endurance is often nothing but endurance. That said, what was I thinking when we were in Chelan? My stream of consciousness went something like this:

Work. Long to-do list for my job at Microsoft. Need to prioritize the website design. I can push the research out a few days. No time for working on my book. Ugh. It'll have to wait. I hope I finish it before the CAR T.

Yeah...it's not a story of cure. But it's a story people with cancer can relate to nonetheless. The book isn't dead. I think there's still benefit. It's not a downer.

The leaves are so green, made luminescent by the sun. Beautiful. Still summer.

Shit—Luke and Sofia are going to drown on that dock. They're going to fall in the water and not be able to get out. Pick yourself up off the couch and go watch them.

Kind of an awkward pause this morning at breakfast when Luke suggested Angela and I buy a retirement home here—as if Angela and I foresee me living that long.

When Sofia grows up, she probably won't even remember me. Or her memories will be faint at best. Luke? Well, he's older. But his memories will fade, too. Still, I've had twelve years with Luke and nine with Sofia. A decent launch pad.

I could be doing a better job parenting. It's not too late.

I wonder if Angela is terrified again.

She and I both felt so free and young on the water today.

I need to check again whether the life insurance is good through age fifty-five. Or is it only age fifty? It's fifty-five. I remember. But I should check again.

I need to lose weight. I hate the feel of belly fat against the waistline of my shorts. And c'mon—make time for at least a few push-ups in the mornings. No excuse.

Luke just called me out on negative self-talk. I was calling myself fat and criticizing myself out loud while standing in the shower for not maintaining a push-up regimen.

We didn't have the money to come here.

We're not bringing that apple pie home. Too messy.

Need to keep Gracie off the furniture. Don't want the homeowners to come back to pug hair.

The kids are having fun. I love watching them in this environment They're happy. I hope they stay that way.

Fortunate enough to steal a final splash of summer in Chelan, WA, despite the leukemia's return (September 2016).

EPILOGUE, OCTOBER 23, 2016

Spoiler alert: The second round of CAR T therapy didn't work for me. Residual blasts remain in my CNS. Just a small number, but they're there, and therefore need to be dealt with.

Dr. Austin and I met a couple of days ago and agreed that we'll probably proceed with some intrathecal chemo (through the Ommaya). And there's some other stuff we'll look at.

Over 150,000 people die on our planet each day. Billions and billions have died since humans first appeared, often painfully and with tragic consequences. What's so special about me?

Not much.

My story is a speck on the back of a speck on the back of a speck in time. And relatively speaking, I've gotten off easy. Angela hasn't. Other people who have lost loved ones or who have children with cancer haven't.

"You don't know how lucky you are," Wendy told Angela tearfully over the phone after her husband, John, whom I came to know when he moved to Seattle for leukemia treatment at the SCCA, passed away post-transplant in 2011.

Wendy was inconsolable.

My story is nothing by comparison. It's trivial.

It took me a while to come around to accepting demise. I

fought it. I went through the oft-quoted five stages of grief. I may be dead by the time you read this. Do I care? Sure. Do I think about it constantly? Well, for a while there—no. With the second round of CAR T not working? Yes, more often.

Ironically, I'm most cognizant of the specter of death when I'm *enjoying* something. *This could all suddenly end.* The thought makes me wistful, not afraid. It also relaxes me when I'm feeling stress. *C'mon, Walt. When you're dead, none of this will matter...* This may sound morbid, but it's not. I see how temporary everything is. How we are *all* mere specks on the back of a speck on the back of a speck in time, no matter who we are, whether president or pauper.

Here's a cliché: facing imminent death, many people run out to do the wild things they've always wanted to do. They jump out of an airplane, take a boat to Antarctica, hang glide in France. Totally get it. Love it. Me, personally? Although adventures sound awesome, I don't have the impulse. I want to live the same life I had before. *I like normal.* Normal is what I want back when you lose it to cancer. I want to watch my kids play soccer, see movies with my wife, have dinner with friends. I don't want to lay in a hospital bed or live in my basement, anxious about the potential for relapse, unable to experience the world outside due to the omnipresent infectious agents that present acute risk to the severely immunosuppressed. The one hundred days of recovery post-transplant when I was stuck at home, unable to go to work, eat out, exercise, play basketball with my kids, or do *anything*, were the worst of my life. The closer the face of mortality has come to mine, the more I've wanted the company of family and friends. That's it.

Although maybe I'll change my mind at some point. I'm thinking about taking the family to the Galapagos Islands. If things end up looking bleak (not yet).

Here's another cliché: near-death experiences change you dramatically; you become a new person. Perhaps. For me, sure—in some ways. But Leukemia didn't magically rid me of hang-ups and bad habits. I still make a conscious effort to self-improve just like anyone else. I didn't suddenly transform into the Dalai Lama.

Cliché number three: near-death experiences give you a new perspective on life.

A brush with mortality is rattling...but it's also settling. It does give you context as to how *fragile* and *fleeting* everything is. I've found I appreciate more and angst less. Time becomes more valuable.

Cliché number four: you draw closer to family and friends. This too is true. Family and friends are the sustenance we need beyond food, air, and water. Mortality brings this into focus.

During my transplant recovery, Angela went on medical leave and stayed home with me for several weeks. I was sad and a little nervous when she went back to work.

My best friend was gone. She did, though, arrange for a series of people to be with me a week or two at a time. The most surprising was my father. He works hard and, as the head of a Kroger subsidiary (at the time), was under immense pressure. Yet he took a leave of absence for an entire two weeks. *That* was love. Seriously. As a fellow workaholic, I get it. That was a sacrifice.[51]

I believe one of two things will happen when I die, whether it's tomorrow or forty years from now. The mental TV will go off, and I will know none the better. I'll be asleep. Without dreams. Or, I'll become part of a universal consciousness—which appeals to my desire to persist and experience what that would be like.

It makes me sad to think of dying early, mostly because I want my kids to have their father—at least for a while. I don't want to leave the parenting of my children to someone else. *I* want to spoil them, teach them, foster their growth into healthy, vibrant adults. No one—no new spouse for Angela or uncle or grandparent—would love my children the way that I do.

Who is the person I worry about *most*? Not my kids, funnily enough. Children are resilient. No, it's Angela I worry about. She would endure—she's tenacious—but it would be hard for her to adjust, not just emotionally, but also on a practical level. I made the wise decision to

---

51   And, of course, my mother's endless generosity with her time—and her putting up with me—was a blessing. And no less appreciated.

purchase a generous life insurance policy when I was younger so our family would be okay financially should something happen to me, but it's not enough for her to coast on if I die. She would need help physically with the house and the kids, which is a lot to ask, particularly because she doesn't have full use of her left arm or leg.

Who knows how what's next. It's a variable I live with and manage, just as we all have variables to contend with.

ACKNOWLEDGEMENTS

I would like to thank all those whose efforts have kept me alive. Among them is, of course, Dr. Tanya Wahl, my oncologist, and the doctors, physician assistants, nurses, technologists, and staff at the following facilities: Swedish Hospital in Seattle, Washington; Overlake Hospital in Bellevue, Washington; El Camino Hospital in Mountain View, California; the University of Washington Medical Center, and the Seattle Cancer Care Alliance. I have survived also thanks to the hard work, intelligence, and dedication of those who have learned to harness our own immune systems as weapons against leukemia and other cancers. I express sincere gratitude to Dr. David Maloney, Dr. Cameron Turtle, and the rest of the research team and staff at the Hutchinson Cancer Research Center as well as those at other research institutions, including Sloan-Kettering, the NIH, and the University of Pennsylvania, whose contributions have helped bring to life CAR T therapy. May we see immunotherapy—and other innovations in cancer treatment—mature, grow, and come to make standard the revolutionary changes and potential benefits they represent.

At the same time, not to get too caught up in the new-new thing, I remind myself not to take for granted the genius behind the stem cell transplant. And there would be no CAR T therapy without chemotherapy (at least not today), a brute force mechanism, but one that has brought me back from the edge several times. Radiation therapy, as ghoulish as it is in the abstract, is also critical to the arsenal. Both chemo and radiation save lives daily.

While the miracle of CAR T has extended my warranty (ok—it did the first time), a wide array of medical science (and the people who administer it) has kept me around. I don't want to risk over-celebrating one treatment since all are important—at least they are today. Further, clinical trials are just that—trials—meaning they're not yet available for everyone, and they don't guarantee cure. So we fight with what we've got while holding out for the next breakthrough, if not for us, for our children.

I would like to express gratitude and love to my stem cell donor and blood-in-law, Matt Jacobsen, for his selflessness, tenacity, integrity, and intrepidness.

Dr. Kathy Gibson—thank you for keeping my feet alive and where they naturally belong (attached to the ends of my legs). Dr. Teresa Girolami—thank you for having the insight that led to the discovery of the aneurysms in my legs.

There are many, many people I want to thank for visiting me in the hospital, taking me to medical appointments, caring for me, bringing me food, spending time with me, holding my job while I was out, helping my family, staying with me for days on end when I was home alone, sending me gifts, writing me thoughtful messages, making introductions to specialists, and connecting with me through my blog. Thank you for that sustenance.

I've dedicated the book to Angela, which is a no-brainer. She and I mockingly call each other sweet names like "daffodil," "pumpkin," and "love muffin" when one of us is behaving badly. We are no Romeo and Juliet, but we love each other. I love Angela because she is kind to the core, smart, funny, tenacious, and ebullient. Plus, she calls bullsh*t when she sees it. Often on me.

I want to express love and gratitude to the people who put their busy lives on hold at different times in the story to fly to Seattle and help take care of me when I was incapacitated or simply needing company, which Angela was wise enough to recognize. These include my father, Doug Harp; my sister, Heather Browning; my cousin Catie Walsh; my sister-in-law Eugenia Lean, and my good friend, Heather Welch. I also want to thank my good friends Mike Green and Stephen Schweiger for flying across the country to visit me when it counted the most. Further, I feel love and appreciation for the many other friends who visited me in the hospital and at different points in my journey, some multiple times. I would try to list them all, but I'm afraid I'll leave someone out. You know who you are. And I haven't forgotten.

Then there's my mom, Sharon Flora. God bless her for her endless generosity. And love to my brother, Porter, for his many stays at various medical facilities throughout the years, and to Eric and Alice Lean for their unwavering support and for keeping our family happy and functional in times of duress.

Regarding the book itself, I owe a great deal of gratitude to friend and author John Shors for his edits and guidance and Heather Welch for her magic sentence-polishing and spot-on suggestions. And I can't forget Lisa Spinazze, the first person to take a "teacher's pen" (literally) to some of the early chapters, as did others after. I will also say that you are very fortunate if you have the opportunity to work with Alice Peck. Her editing has been invaluable. Ruth Mullen is wonderful as well.

Finally, a big hug (or manly chest bump) to those who took the time to read parts—or all—of the manuscript over the years, sometimes more than once, providing both encouragement and honest, constructive criticism. The book is what it is largely because of them. I'm sure I'm going to forget someone, but here is a list of those who contributed along the way in ways both large and small: Angela Lean, Arichica Holt Prescott, Bonnie McCracken, Brian Lurie, Catherine Walsh, Cindy Rockfeld, Clint Walters,

Dan Lewis, David Schaaf, Doug Harp, Elpida Argenziano, Emily Carrion, Erin Martin, Gloria Wolfe, Heather Welch, Jeene Brown, Jeff Hsu, Ken Wolfe, Kevin Ascher, Laurie Saito, Leaf, Leland Flora, Lisa Spinazze, Liz Friedman, Luke Harp, Malinda McCollum, Matt McIlwain, Michael Wegmann, Patricia Ramirez, Phil Friedman, Pooja Vithlani, Porter Harp, Rachel Schwartz, Renee Borger Murphy, Sarah Goodman Hulquist, Scott Rockfeld, Shailendra Tiwari, Sharon Flora, Sheryl Tullis, Sofia Harp, Steve Schweiger, Susan Szafir, Tanya Wahl, and Tiffany Spencer.

Thank you to the talented Vanessa Maynard for the cover and interior design and Jay Yun for the cover photo. Kudos to Luke Harp for the composite photo of Gracie (our pug) and the design of the LS Publishing logo.

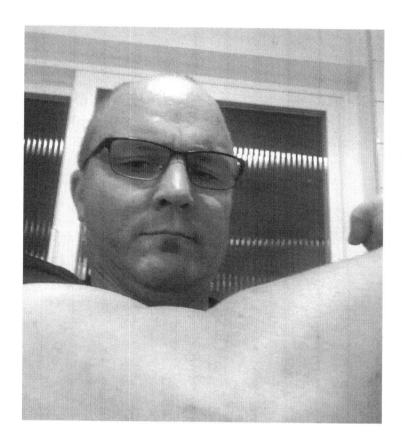

Selfie just four days after second-round CAR T cell infusion. (6:37 a.m., Sunday, October 2, 2016). Wondering if the treatment was working.

ABOUT THE AUTHOR

Walter Harp lives with his wife, two children, and a sedentary rescue pug on Mercer Island, a friendly island community of almost twenty-five thousand located on Lake Washington, just outside of Seattle. Walter enjoys good storytelling, whether it's a movie or book; spending time with his family and friends, vinyasa yoga—even if he rarely has time to go—and all kinds of food. He's also an admitted workaholic, but not incorrigible.

Made in the USA
Middletown, DE
17 October 2017